BLAST OFF!™

North Carolina
Reading

Book 4

EXAMINATION COPY
DO NOT DUPLICATE
©BUCKLE DOWN PUBLISHING CO.

 Buckle Down
PUBLISHING COMPANY

Acknowledgments

Excerpt from Chapter 8 of LITTLE PET SHOP OF HORRORS: BONECHILLERS 2 by Betsy Haynes. Copyright © 1994 by Betsy Haynes and Daniel Weiss Associates, Inc. Reprinted by permission of HarperCollins Publishers, Inc.

Excerpt from CAT WALK by Mary Stolz. Copyright © 1983 by Mary Stolz. Reprinted by permission of Roslyn Targ Literary Agency, Inc.

Excerpt from JENNIFER MURDLEY'S TOAD. Copyright © 1992 by Bruce Coville. Reprinted by permission of Harcourt Brace & Company.

Excerpt from MORGAN'S ZOO by James Howe. Copyright © 1984 by James Howe. Reprinted by permission of Writers House Inc.

"Young Night Thoughts" by Robert Louis Stevenson. Public Domain.

Every effort has been made by the publisher to locate each owner of the copyrighted material reprinted in this publication and to secure the necessary permissions. If there are any questions regarding the use of these materials, the publisher will take appropriate corrective measures to acknowledge ownership in future publications.

ISBN 0-7836-1490-X

Catalog #BF NC4R 1

6 7 8 9 10

Copyright © 1997 by Buckle Down Publishing Company, a subsidiary of Profiles Corporation. All rights reserved. No part of this work may be reproduced or transmitted in any form or by any means, electronic or mechanical, including photocopying, recording, or any information storage or retrieval systems, except as may be expressly permitted in writing by the publisher, Buckle Down Publishing, P.O. Box 2180, Iowa City, IA 52244-2180.

Cover art: Images © 1996 PhotoDisc, Inc.

TABLE OF CONTENTS

Introduction

What's on the Test?

The fourth-grade test includes poetry, made-up stories (fiction), and writings that are about real people, places, things, or events (nonfiction). Some of the passages will be interesting. Some may make you want to snooze.

After you read each passage, you'll be asked to answer questions about it. Each question will give you four answer choices. Your job on each of these questions will be to choose the *best* answer. Some questions will have special kinds of drawings called "graphic organizers." These drawings help you to better understand what you have read in the passage. You've probably learned how to use graphic organizers in school.

What's in *Blast Off! North Carolina Reading*?

Good readers use different methods for different types of reading. Some students can read a book or magazine easily but still have trouble when they get to a reading test. If you are one of these people, don't worry. What you probably need are a few methods to help you read for the special purpose of attacking a reading test. And that is what this workbook is all about!

Blast Off! North Carolina Reading will help you do your best on the state test by reviewing basic reading skills. These skills are important—not just for school but for your entire life.

Blast Off! will help you prepare to answer the kinds of questions that you'll see on the state test. It will also teach you some test-taking tips that will help you do your best in any subject.

Are You the Hare or the Tortoise?

Remember the story about the tortoise and the hare? The hare, a naturally swift runner, thought racing against a tortoise would be a piece of cake. So after he got a good start, he goofed off and even took a nap.

© 1997 Profiles Corporation. DO NOT DUPLICATE.

The tortoise, a natural-born slowpoke, knew it wouldn't be easy to win the race. But he believed in himself and kept on moving toward the finish line. Do you remember who won? The slow but steady tortoise. He faced a difficult task, but he never quit. His positive attitude paid off.

What about you? Do you read as well as a hare can run? Or do you read as slowly and carefully as a tortoise walks? On the state reading test, speed isn't really important. What *is* important is that you keep moving along, doing your best throughout the test. Steady work and a positive attitude will make you a winner on the North Carolina reading test.

A Training Program for Readers

Great athletes don't just wake up one morning and decide to run a marathon. They follow training programs. A training program helps an athlete improve on his or her natural abilities. You can have a training program for reading, too.

Think about it: What's the most important part of training to be a runner? Running, of course. If an athlete wants to be a super runner, he or she has to run—a lot. If you want to be a super reader, you have to read—a lot. It doesn't matter so much what you read, just that you read a little bit every day.

This doesn't mean you always have to read books. Reading material is everywhere. The list below gives a few ideas you might try. Add your own ideas as you think of them, or ask your classmates to share their ideas.

❏ fast-food menus (McDonalds, Burger King, Kentucky Fried Chicken, etc.)

❏ cereal boxes

❏ the back of your toothpaste tube

❏ billboards

❏ movie reviews

❏ yellow page ads for skateboards, bicycles, or whatever interests you

❏ a recipe for your favorite kind of cookie or cake (You might even want to bake it for your family.)

❏ a newspaper article about your favorite sports team

❏ the comic strips in your local newspaper

❏ all the fortunes in a package of fortune cookies

❏ all the jokes in a copy of *Reader's Digest*

❏ _____

❏ _____

❏ _____

❏ _____

© 1997 Profiles Corporation. DO NOT DUPLICATE.

Fire Up Your Reading Skills with *Blast Off!*

In each lesson of this book, you'll review a type of question often asked on reading tests. Then you'll have one or two practice passages with questions like the ones covered in the lesson.

If you study each lesson carefully, you won't see any surprises on test day. You'll know exactly what to expect on the reading test, and you'll be able to answer all the different types of questions. You'll become more confident as you see your skills improve. If you study hard now, you're sure to do well on the test.

General Tips for Taking Reading Tests

Taking the North Carolina reading test is a lot like playing a game, such as soccer or kickball. Being a good player requires skill. And to gain skill you have to *practice*.

Getting a good score in the Reading Test Game also depends on your skill level. Fortunately, you can increase your reading skills with practice.

Below are a few general reading tips to get you started.

 First, read every word of the passage.

Don't skip over anything. Read the entire passage before looking at the questions. Reading every word will help you find out what the passage is *mainly* about. And it will also help you remember where to go to find answers to the questions.

When reading the passage, you can slow down and go back over a difficult idea. But don't stop or get stuck. Keep moving until you come to the end of the passage.

 Learn how to answer the different types of questions.

There are several types of questions that you're likely to see on the state reading test. Each lesson in this book explains a type of test question and gives you tips on how to answer it.

© 1997 Profiles Corporation. DO NOT DUPLICATE.

Tip 3 **Use information from the passage to choose your answer.**

You're being tested on how well you read, not on how much you know about the topic of the passage. Be sure to use the information in the reading passage to answer the questions.

Tip 4 **Read every question carefully.**

Read slowly and carefully. Don't jump ahead and select an answer before you've read the entire question and all the answer choices.

Tip 5 **Use key words to find the answer.**

If you can identify key words in the question, you'll improve your chances of quickly finding the answer in the passage. This book will help you identify key words.

Tip 6 **Answer every question, even if you have to guess.**

If you don't know an answer on the test, give it your best guess. Cross out the answers that you know are wrong and pick from the ones that are left. You won't be any worse off, and you might improve your score. If you don't answer a question, you can't possibly get it right.

Tip 7 **Have fun.**

Just like a runner training for a race, you will be "in training" for the state reading test. When the test date rolls around, you'll be ready—"in shape"—for the test. And because you'll be ready, you can relax and have fun with it.

On your mark, get set, *go!*

© 1997 Profiles Corporation. DO NOT DUPLICATE.

Big Ideas and Small Details

UNIT 1

Lesson 1

Getting the Main Idea

The main idea of a reading passage tells what it is *mostly* about. Sometimes the author puts the main idea in a sentence. Sometimes you have to figure it out on your own.

Read the paragraph below from *About Animals*, a Childcraft book.

You can always tell a turtle by its shell. A box turtle has a high, round shell that it can close up like a box. A map turtle has a wide, flat shell with bumpy edges. A soft-shelled turtle's shell looks like a green pancake.

1. Which sentence from the paragraph tells what the paragraph is *mostly* about?

_____

_____

© 1997 Profiles Corporation. DO NOT DUPLICATE.

Sometimes the main idea isn't stated in a sentence. You have to read the passage and figure out the main idea on your own.

Read the following paragraph from *A Cricket in Times Square* by George Selden. Then write a sentence that tells the main idea.

> "Catch the mouse!" shouted Mama. She picked up a *Fortune* magazine—very big and heavy—and heaved it after Tucker. It hit him on the left hind leg just as he vanished into the drain pipe.

2. What is the main idea of the paragraph?

_____

_____

_____

Main Idea Tips

Following are some tips to help you find the main idea of a reading passage.

 Tip 1 **Read the entire passage first.**

This is important. Before you can find the main idea of a passage, you have to read the whole passage.

Tip 2 **Decide whether the passage is fiction or nonfiction.**

Nonfiction passages are about real things. Fiction passages are about made-up things. Many nonfiction passages, like the paragraph on turtles, will tell you the main idea in a sentence. Most fiction passages, like the sentences from *A Cricket in Times Square*, will not. If you want to know the main idea of a fiction passage, you almost always have to figure it out on your own.

© 1997 Profiles Corporation. DO NOT DUPLICATE.

Practice Passage

Directions: Read the passage below and use it to apply the tips in this unit.

When I was ten, my grandfather came to live with us. I'd never even seen him before; he was a stranger to me. Mom said that for twenty-five years he'd been the foreman on a cattle ranch in California. When Gramps showed up, I was surprised. He seemed too young to be eighty. He easily walked without a cane, though he did have a walking stick.

Just about all Gramps did that first week was whittle his stick. He sat on the back porch, wearing a cowboy hat that looked too big for him, took a knife out of his pocket, and began to carve at the handle. He silently whittled away the hours while a pile of curled wood chips grew beside him.

One day after I got home from school, I found him rubbing his walking stick with a piece of fine sandpaper. "How's it going, Gramps?" I asked.

"Not so bad, Toby," he said. His big hat hid his face, but I could see his fingers working. When he blew the sawdust away, I saw the head of a horse carved into his stick.

"Wow!" I said.

"This is Paloma, the horse your grandmother and I had when we panned for gold."

"You really panned for gold?" I asked. Gramps was starting to look different to me. His hat didn't even seem so big anymore. I sat down next to him as he worked.

"It was long before your time, Toby. Before your mother's, too," Gramps said. "Your Grandma Clara and I lived in an old canvas tent on the banks of a stream in the Sierra Madre mountains. And no," he said, answering the unspoken question in my eyes, "we never did strike it rich. But Clara and I didn't mind. We made enough to get us to our next adventure."

"I suppose you went hunting for lost gold mines," I said, joking.

"Now that's a whole other story," he said. ❖❖

EXAMINATION COPY
DO NOT DUPLICATE
©BUCKLE DOWN PUBLISHING CO.

© 1997 Profiles Corporation. DO NOT DUPLICATE.

List the important parts of the passage.

If you can figure out what is important in the passage, you'll be able to state the main idea. On the lines below, write three important parts of the passage you just read.

3. _____

4. _____

5. _____

Tip 4 **Look for a sentence that tells the main idea. If no main idea is stated, put it in your own words.**

Look back at the story. Is there a single sentence that tells the main idea?

6. Think about the important parts of the story you listed under tip #3. Use them to write the main idea on the lines below.

_____

_____

_____

Tip 5 **Look for the main idea in the answer choices.**

You've written the main idea in your own words. Now see if you can find it in the answer choices.

7. What is the *main* idea of the passage?
   A. Toby's grandfather lived on a cattle ranch.
   B. Toby is getting to know his grandfather.
   C. Toby's grandfather once owned a horse.
   D. Toby is learning how to whittle.

© 1997 Profiles Corporation. DO NOT DUPLICATE.

Answer A is a fact from the story. It helps us understand a little about Gramps. But it isn't the main idea.

Answer B tells the main idea of the story. Toby is getting to know his grandfather.

Answer C tells us just a little bit about Gramps, but it isn't the main idea.

Answer D is not an idea in the passage. Does the passage say that Toby is learning how to whittle?

 Main idea questions can be asked in different ways.

A main idea question doesn't always ask, "What is the main idea?" It might say,

"Which sentence *best* tells about this passage?"

Or it might say something like,

"Which of the following would be a good title for this passage?"

Either way, the question is still asking you to find the main idea.

 Compare the main idea of the passage to a situation in the real world.

Compare the main idea of the passage to another situation that is similar. Doing this will help you to better understand the main idea. Look at the question below:

8. Which of these experiences would help you *most* to understand the story?
   A. taking a trip to a cattle ranch in California
   B. taking lessons in how to carve wood figures
   C. riding a horse in the Smoky Mountains
   D. visiting with an older family member

We already figured out the main idea in question 7. What was it?

_____

Now look at the answer choices in question 8. Which choice is most like the main idea of the story?

_____

© 1997 Profiles Corporation. DO NOT DUPLICATE.

Sample Main Idea Questions

Directions: Circle the correct answer for each question.

1. Which sentence *best* tells about this passage?
   A. Now that Toby's grandfather has come to live with him, Toby learns about Gramps' life.
   B. Toby's grandfather whittled a horse's head on top of his walking stick.
   C. Toby's grandparents once lived in a tent next to a stream while they panned for gold.
   D. Toby's grandfather tells him about a horse he owned long ago.

2. Which of the following would be a good title for this story?
   A. "Mining Country"
   B. "Guide to Whittling"
   C. "The History of Cattle Ranching"
   D. "Getting to Know Gramps"

© 1997 Profiles Corporation. DO NOT DUPLICATE.

Additional Practice Questions

Directions: Now try answering some other kinds of questions about the reading passage. Circle the correct answer for each question. You'll learn more about these question types in other units of this book.

3. How long had Gramps worked on a cattle ranch?

   A. one week

   B. ten years

   C. twenty-five years

   D. eighty years

4. Why didn't Gramps seem to mind that he hadn't "struck it rich" as a gold miner?

   A. He and Clara didn't like panning for gold.

   B. He earned enough money to do other interesting things.

   C. He had planned to go to work on a cattle ranch.

   D. He earned enough money to buy a horse.

5. Who was Clara?

   A. Toby's mother

   B. Gramps' horse

   C. Gramps' wife

   D. Toby's sister

EXAMINATION COPY
DO NOT DUPLICATE
©BUCKLE DOWN PUBLISHING CO.

6. What is the *best* strategy to use to answer question #5?

   A. Skim the passage for the name *Clara*.

   B. Make a list of all the names mentioned in the passage.

   C. Read the first sentence of every paragraph.

   D. Reread the entire passage carefully.

7. What does Gramps mean when he says, "Now that's a whole other story"?

   A. He has another story to tell Toby.

   B. He wants Toby to write a story for him.

   C. He doesn't know the answer to Toby's question.

   D. The tales he's telling Toby aren't really true.

© 1997 Profiles Corporation. DO NOT DUPLICATE.

Lesson 2

Details, Details, Details

Details are the facts and descriptions that add interest to a reading passage. Without them, reading would be pretty dull.

Practice Passage

Directions: Read the following passage to learn more about detail questions.

In 1894, Bessie Smith was born into a poor family in Chattanooga, Tennessee. As a little girl, she sang to the world while standing outside her family's run-down house. Her songs were simple and her voice was strong and beautiful to hear.

Bessie performed for the first time when she was about eight years old. Her brother Andrew played his guitar while she danced and sang on a street corner in Chattanooga. People walking by tossed money to them.

When she was 18 years old, Bessie met a famous singer named Ma Rainey. "Let your soul do the singing," Ma told her. And Bessie did. Her sad songs told of the hard life she had lived and the troubles she had suffered.

Bessie sang a type of music called *blues*. The blues grew out of the many different kinds of music sung and played by African Americans in the 1800s. Many blues songs are about loneliness and sorrow. Others are about people keeping their strength and sense of humor in times of trouble.

Bessie's music deeply touched the people who heard her sing. She was so popular in the 1920s that she became the highest paid African American entertainer in the country. From Detroit to New Orleans, traffic jams developed around theaters where she performed. Bessie's popularity helped bring the blues to a wider audience. The young singer soon became known as the "Empress of the Blues."

Bessie made over 150 recordings during her lifetime. Her music influenced many other singers who came after her. When Bessie died in 1937, a marker was placed on her grave. It reads, "The Greatest Blues Singer Will Never Stop Singing." ❖❖

© 1997 Profiles Corporation. DO NOT DUPLICATE.

Details Tips

Detail questions are usually the easiest types of questions to answer. Following are some tips to help you answer questions about the passage you just read.

 Identify the main idea.

The most important details are the ones that support the main idea. To understand which details are important, you first need to know the main idea of the passage.

1. What is the main idea of the passage?

_____

 Look for details that support the main idea.

The main idea of a reading passage is like the roof of a house. A roof is supported by walls. The main idea of a passage is supported by details in the passage.

If a wall stands a few feet from the roof, it can't hold the roof up. In the same way, details that have nothing to do with the main idea can't support the main idea. If the details don't support the main idea, then those details aren't the most important ones.

2. In the graphic organizer below, write in two more important details that support the main idea of the passage.

Main Idea
Bessie Smith was a great blues singer.

Supporting Detail	Supporting Detail	Supporting Detail
• Bessie began singing as a little girl.		
• Bessie's music deeply touched people.		

© 1997 Profiles Corporation. DO NOT DUPLICATE.

Tip 3   **Identify a key word in the question. Skim the passage to find the key word. Then read the sentences that surround the key word.**

Read each question carefully. Look for the most important word or phrase (group of words) in the question. These words are usually easy to find when you skim the reading passage.

3. Read the question below and circle key words or phrases that might help you find the answer in the passage.

    Where did Bessie first earn money for performing?

Skimming means to run your eyes quickly over the reading material while looking for something. Skim the reading passage to find the key words that you circled in the question above. Go back to the passage and read the sentences containing those words.

Now read the question again. (It is reprinted below.) Then read the answer choices and choose the correct answer.

4. Where did Bessie first earn money for performing?
   A. on a street corner in her hometown
   B. at a theater in Detroit
   C. outside her family's house
   D. at a theater in Chattanooga

 Tip 4   **To determine the order in which events occur, skim the passage to find key words from the answer choices.**

Some detail questions may ask which event happened first, next, or last.

Circle the key words in the following answer choices. Then skim the passage to find the key words. Read the sentences containing those words. Use the information you gathered to answer the question.

5. Which of the following happened *first*?
   A. Bessie became the highest-paid African American entertainer.
   B. Bessie became known as the "Empress of the Blues."
   C. Bessie met Ma Rainey.
   D. Bessie made over 150 recordings.

© 1997 Profiles Corporation. DO NOT DUPLICATE.

Cross out choices that aren't based on ideas in the passage.

Correct answers to detail questions are always based on ideas from the passage. This means that answers not based on ideas in the passage will not be correct.

Look at the following question. Cross out the choices that are NOT supported by the passage.

6. What happened to Bessie after she met Ma Rainey?
    A. She became a popular singer herself.
    B. She became even poorer.
    C. She stopped singing sad songs.
    D. She never went back to Chattanooga.

Is choice A an idea from the passage? Did Bessie become a popular singer? Yes. Keep choice A.

Answer B is not an idea in the passage. Nothing is mentioned about Bessie becoming poorer. In fact, it says that she was highly paid. Cross out B.

Answer C is not an idea in the passage. Bessie continued to sing sad songs. Her songs "told of the hard life she had lived and the troubles she had suffered." Cross out C.

Answer D is not an idea in the passage. The passage does not say that Bessie never returned to Chattanooga. Cross out D.

Choice A is the best answer.

© 1997 Profiles Corporation. DO NOT DUPLICATE.

Sample Detail Questions

Directions: Circle the correct answer for each question.

1. How old was Bessie when she met Ma Rainey?
    A. 8 years old
    B. 18 years old
    C. 20 years old
    D. 37 years old

2. Based on the passage, which of the following does *not* describe the blues?
    A. a type of music that expresses loneliness and sorrow
    B. songs about people dealing with times of trouble
    C. music that grew out of earlier forms of African American music
    D. songs that are about happiness and celebration

3. Which phrase *best* describes the songs Bessie sang?
    A. fast and cheerful
    B. lonely and unpleasant
    C. simple and sad
    D. slow and happy

4. Which of the following happened *last*?
    A. Bessie performed in theaters around the country.
    B. Bessie met a famous singer.
    C. Bessie sang outside her family's house.
    D. Bessie performed with her brother Andrew.

© 1997 Profiles Corporation. DO NOT DUPLICATE.

Additional Practice Questions

Directions: Now try answering some other kinds of questions about the reading passage. Circle the correct answer for each question.

5. Which of the following statements is an opinion?
   A. "... she became the highest paid African American entertainer. ..."
   B. "Bessie sang a type of music called the *blues*."
   C. "... her voice was strong and beautiful to hear."
   D. "People walking by tossed money to them."

6. What caused the traffic jams described in the passage?
   A. the people rushing to buy Bessie's records
   B. the cars that brought Bessie's band to the theater
   C. the people who tossed money to Bessie and Andrew
   D. the crowd of people going to see Bessie's performances

7. What does the author mean when she says that Bessie "influenced" other singers?
   A. Other singers refused to sing the blues.
   B. Other singers placed a marker on her grave.
   C. Other singers learned from the way Bessie sang.
   D. Other singers tried to make as many recordings as Bessie.

8. Which of these experiences would help you *most* to understand this passage?
   A. listening to some of Bessie Smith's recordings
   B. reading a travel book about the state of Tennessee
   C. reading a newspaper article on a current blues musician
   D. watching a film on the history of theaters in the United States

9. Which of the following would be a good title for this passage?
   A. "How to Become a Famous Musician"
   B. "Ma Rainey: Her Life and Times"
   C. "Bessie Smith: Empress of the Blues"
   D. "Famous Songs of the Twentieth Century"

© 1997 Profiles Corporation. DO NOT DUPLICATE.

Unit 1 Review

Directions: Read the passage below and answer the questions that follow.

From

LITTLE
PET SHOP
of
HORRORS

by Betsy Haynes

Cassidy Cavanaugh suspected something was strange about the mysterious new pet shop. The sign in the window promised "custom pets" to fill any order. When Cassie visited the shop, she thought the animals stared at her with sad eyes. Several seemed to be trying to tell her something. And the owner, Mr. Willard—with his bulging, unblinking eyes and stale breath—was downright creepy.

What was that terrible scream from the back room? Cassie intended to find out, but Mr. Willard stopped her. Then Cassie overheard mean David Ferrante ordering a golden retriever. Before she could get to the door, she began to feel hot and dizzy. "Here, drink this," Mr. Willard had said as he handed her a glass of sweet pink liquid. Cassie drank it; then she fainted.

Cassie felt as if she were trapped in a whirlpool, struggling to the surface from the depths of a deep black sea. The closer to the surface she got, the brighter it became. The hum in her head slowly faded away.

"It's okay, Cassidy. Everything's fine, girl."

Her eyes fluttered open, and she looked up into Mr. Willard's smiling face. He was reaching toward her. He had something in his beefy hand. *It was a dog collar!*

"Good girl, Cassidy. Good girl," Mr. Willard said in a soothing voice. "You'll be going home soon."

Cassie cringed as Mr. Willard's hand came closer. Trying desperately to back away, she bumped to a stop against something hard. She looked around in a panic. There was nowhere to go! She was in a small metal cage. Mr. Willard fastened the collar around Cassie's neck. Then he slammed the cage door closed and locked it.

"No!" Cassie yelled at him. *"Don't! There's been some mistake!"*

But no words came out. All that came from Cassie's mouth were loud barks. She tried again. *"Let me out of here! I want to go home!"*

© 1997 Profiles Corporation. DO NOT DUPLICATE.

"Shut up your stupid yapping," shouted Mr. Willard.

"Please let me out of here! My parents will be looking for me if I'm not home immediately, and then you'll be in big trouble!"

Mr. Willard's eyes narrowed. He reached through the bars and grabbed the collar, pulling Cassie forward until her nose was mashed against the bars.

She yelped with pain.

"Didn't you hear me?" he said, clenching his teeth and putting his face close to hers. His breath smelled worse than ever. "You'd better shut up. . . ."

Cassie looked into his watery black eyes. She knew he meant what he said.

He let go of her collar. With a massive effort he struggled to his feet. He stood glaring down at her.

She didn't dare move. Or make a sound. Her heart was racing. Cassie had never been so frightened in her life.

She looked down at her arms, and a shudder went through her body. They were completely covered with thick blond fur. She looked at her hands. But all she saw were furry paws! She crossed her eyes and looked down her nose. The tip of it was much too far away. . . .

Cassie turned and looked behind her. Her body was long and hairy. At the very end of her body Cassie saw—a tail!

Oh, no! she thought. *I'm a—I'm a dog! A half-grown golden retriever. And I'm locked in a cage!* She was a prisoner. Helpless. She couldn't even *talk.*

"One more custom pet, ready for delivery," Mr. Willard said. A sinister smile spread across his fat face. "Oh, what a story you could tell if you could talk, Cassidy." He cackled wildly. "But no one will ever understand your miserable barking."

He threw back his head and laughed hysterically. His huge belly bounced with each chuckle. Mr. Willard was still laughing as he waddled across the store and disappeared into the back room.

Frantically Cassie threw herself against the cage door, trying with all her might to get out. She pawed at the lock, but without fingers she couldn't begin to open it. She bit at it in frustration. That didn't work either. In her desperation she rammed the bars over and over with her shoulders until she was aching and bruised. Finally she sank to the floor in defeat.

She was a dog!

And she was trapped. ❖❖

© 1997 Profiles Corporation. DO NOT DUPLICATE.

Unit 1 Review Questions

Directions: Circle the correct answer for each question.

1. Which answer *best* completes the graphic organizer?

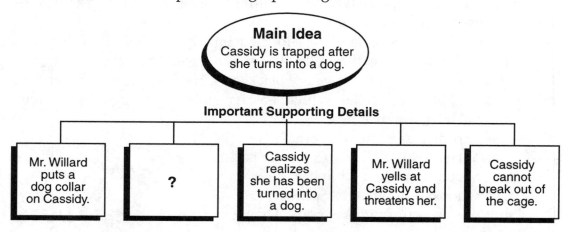

A. Cassidy purchases a pet.

B. The animals stare sadly at Cassidy.

C. Mr. Willard has stale breath.

D. Mr. Willard locks Cassidy in a cage.

2. What does Cassidy want to do when she gets out of the cage?

A. go home to her parents

B. bite Mr. Willard's hand

C. give the collar back to Mr. Willard

D. bark at her new owner

3. How does Cassidy *first* know that she has turned into a dog?

A. Mr. Willard won't do what she asks.

B. She has a collar around her neck.

C. She sees that her arms are covered with fur.

D. She feels trapped in a whirlpool.

4. If you wanted to retell this story to a friend, which would be the most important point to remember?

A. David Ferrante is a mean person.

B. A pet shop owner is turning people into pets.

C. Mr. Willard's belly bounces when he chuckles.

D. Cassidy's dog fur is blonde.

5. Which of the following events happened *first*?

A. Cassidy tried to break out of the cage.

B. Cassidy barked at Mr. Willard.

C. Cassidy saw that she had the body of a dog.

D. Mr. Willard put the dog collar on Cassidy.

© 1997 Profiles Corporation. DO NOT DUPLICATE.

Additional Practice Questions

Directions: Now try answering some other kinds of questions about the reading passage. Circle the correct answer for each question.

6. What does Mr. Willard plan to do with Cassidy?
   A. turn her back into a girl and let her go
   B. sell her to someone who has ordered a custom pet
   C. teach her to bark like a dog
   D. have her guard his pet shop

7. Which word *best* describes how Cassidy feels when Mr. Willard approaches her with the dog collar?
   A. playful
   B. scared
   C. disappointed
   D. friendly

8. What does Mr. Willard mean when he says, "Oh, what a story you could tell if you could talk, Cassidy"?
   A. If Cassidy could speak instead of bark, she could let people know that Mr. Willard is turning children into dogs.
   B. If Cassidy were able to talk, she could entertain people with an interesting story that would make them laugh.
   C. If Cassidy hadn't lost the ability to make sounds, people would be able to understand what happened to her.
   D. If she could speak, she would not make as much noise as when she barks.

9. What does Mr. Willard mean when he tells Cassidy to "Shut up your stupid yapping"?
   A. "Stop crying."
   B. "Stop talking."
   C. "Stop barking."
   D. "Stop whining."

10. What is *most likely* to happen next in the story?
    A. Cassidy will break the cage's lock with her strong teeth.
    B. Mr. Willard will turn Cassidy back into a girl.
    C. Cassidy will be sold as a pet but she will escape.
    D. Cassidy will be turned into another kind of animal.

© 1997 Profiles Corporation. DO NOT DUPLICATE.

Parts of a Story

Lesson 3

Understanding Characters and Setting

Fiction passages always have **characters**. They may be animals, people, or even imaginary beings like talking shoes or a friendly monster. Usually, a short story will have only one or two important characters. A book, on the other hand, is likely to have several important characters.

Stories also have a **setting**. The setting is the place and time in which the story occurs. Sometimes a story may take place in more than one setting.

Character and Setting Tips

Following are some tips to help you identify the character and setting in a story.

 Tip 1 **Look for details about the characters.**

Finding out about characters is mostly a matter of paying attention to details.

Read the paragraph below and answer the questions that follow.

> Kelly marched across the playground toward Junior Becker. She was the smallest student in her class, but she seemed about as small as a thunderstorm at that moment. Just the look in her dark brown eyes would've been enough to knock most kids over. She'd rolled up the sleeves of her baggy black sweatshirt and was pulling her little brother Ben behind her. Ben

© 1997 Profiles Corporation. DO NOT DUPLICATE.

was still wiping the mashed peanut butter and jelly sandwich from his blond hair. Kelly's friends—Mara, Shelley, and Alisha—were there, too, running behind her, telling her to forget about it.

"Not until Junior apologizes," Kelly said.

Just ahead, by the dumpster, stood Junior—thick as a tree trunk and surrounded by his goofy friends.

1. How many friends are with Kelly? _____

2. What does Kelly look like?

   _____

   _____

3. Tell one detail about Ben:

   _____

   _____

4. Tell one detail about Junior:

   _____

   _____

5. Which character is angry?
   A. Mara   C. Junior Becker
   B. Kelly   D. Alisha

6. Who is pulling Ben by the hand?
   A. Kelly   C. Shelley
   B. Alisha   D. Junior Becker

7. How old is Ben?
   A. the same age as Kelly   C. younger than Kelly
   B. older than Kelly   D. older than Junior

© 1997 Profiles Corporation. DO NOT DUPLICATE.

"Listen" as the author introduces you to the characters.

In real life, you might learn about someone by listening to other people talk. When you read, you can get to know the characters by "listening" to what the author has to say about them.

Read the passage below from *Encyclopedia Brown and the Case of the Mysterious Handprints* by Donald J. Sobol. Then answer the questions that follow.

> Only his parents and teachers called him by his real name, Leroy. Everyone else called him Encyclopedia.
>
> An encyclopedia is a book or set of books filled with facts from A to Z. So was Encyclopedia's head. He had read more books than anyone in Idaville, and he never forgot what he read. His pals insisted that he was better than a library.

8. Which word *best* describes Leroy?
   A. smart   C. carefree
   B. friendly   D. rude

9. According to the passage, which sentence tells how Leroy's friends *most likely* feel about him?
   A. They are jealous of his good memory.
   B. They are proud to be his friends.
   C. They want to prove that he can forget things.
   D. They don't believe he can remember things.

 Pay attention to how the characters act.

You can learn a lot about characters by how they act in different situations.

The passage below is from *The Beast in Ms. Rooney's Room* by Patricia Reilly Giff. It tells about a boy named Richard Best on the first day of school. The girl who sits across from him has just smiled at Richard.

> He frowned at her. Then he pulled in his breath. Sniffing loudly, he stuck the eraser end of his new pencil up his nose.
> He shook his head. The pencil swung back and forth gently.
> The girl looked as if she were going to throw up.
> Good.

© 1997 Profiles Corporation. DO NOT DUPLICATE.

Answer the following questions.

10. What did Richard do *after* the girl smiled at him?
    A. He threw up.
    B. He gave her his eraser.
    C. He asked to borrow her pencil.
    D. He stuck a pencil in his nose.

11. What do Richard's actions *most likely* say about him?
    A. He is a friendly boy.
    B. He likes to upset people.
    C. He has a cold.
    D. He likes the smell of pencils.

 Decide how the characters are alike or different from each other.

Sometimes an author will compare characters in the story. This can help the reader understand how the characters are alike or different from each other.

Read the following passage from *How Juan Got Home* by Peggy Mann.

> Juan kept talking almost nonstop all the way. He had so much talk inside him it seemed he just couldn't get it all said.
> Carlos spoke very little. When they had finished piling the boxes in a corner of the basement, Carlos explained why he always answered Juan in such short sentences. He knew very little Spanish.

12. Fill in the diagram to show one way in which Carlos and Juan are different from each other.

Juan	Carlos

© 1997 Profiles Corporation. DO NOT DUPLICATE.

Look for details that tell you where and when the story takes place.

Read the paragraph below from *Tornado!* by Walter R. Brown and Norman D. Anderson. Then answer the questions that follow.

> The trim fifteen-year-old girl glanced over her shoulder at the tumbling, swirling mass of black clouds that nearly covered the Michigan sky. It was the third week in March, 1976.

13. Where does the story take place?

_____

14. When does the story take place?

_____

15. What event is taking place at the time of the story?

_____

© 1997 Profiles Corporation. DO NOT DUPLICATE.

Practice Passage

Directions: Read the passage below to learn more about character and setting questions.

Shawna and Diana shared a bedroom. They were sisters, but they were as different as two sisters could be.

Shawna always put her things away. She liked to clean her room, then lie on her bed and read. But Diana always made a mess of everything. She left books, shoes, and games all over the place. She liked to listen to very loud music.

The two girls were always fighting.

"I'm tired of having your things all over the room!" Shawna would say. "And turn down that music!"

"I'm tired of you picking up my things!" Diana would say. "I don't touch your things."

Then one day Shawna had an idea. "Why don't we put a line across the floor?" she said. "We'll pretend it's a wall. You can stay on your side of the room. I'll stay on my side."

They found a big roll of tape. Then they put a line across the middle of the room.

It didn't work. Diana still left her things on Shawna's side of the room. Shawna still picked up Diana's things. The tape just wasn't enough, so they put up a row of chairs. Next they pulled their big bookcases into the middle of the room. At last they could both do what they wanted.

The first night, Shawna said, "Hey, are you still there?"

The next night, Diana said, "Can I come see you? I miss you."

The third night, Shawna said, "This is a dumb idea. I don't like it."

"I hate it too," Diana said. "Maybe we could just try to get along."

"That sounds good to me," Shawna said. ❖❖

© 1997 Profiles Corporation. DO NOT DUPLICATE.

Sample Character and Setting Questions

Directions: Circle the correct answer for each question.

1. Who are Diana and Shawna?
   A. sisters
   B. best friends
   C. next-door neighbors
   D. cousins

2. Where does the story take place?
   A. in a library
   B. in a bedroom
   C. in a backyard
   D. in a family room

3. How do the girls behave most of the time when they are together?
   A. They don't pay much attention to each other.
   B. They build things together.
   C. They play music and have fun together.
   D. They argue a lot about their differences.

4. How does Shawna feel about Diana leaving her things all over the room?
   A. glad
   B. sad
   C. angry
   D. jealous

5. How do the girls' feelings toward each other change during the story?
   A. from mad to bored
   B. from happy to sad
   C. from angry to friendly
   D. from sad to puzzled

EXAMINATION COPY DO NOT DUPLICATE ©BUCKLE DOWN PUBLISHING CO.

© 1997 Profiles Corporation. DO NOT DUPLICATE.

6. Which answer *best* completes this diagram or character map?

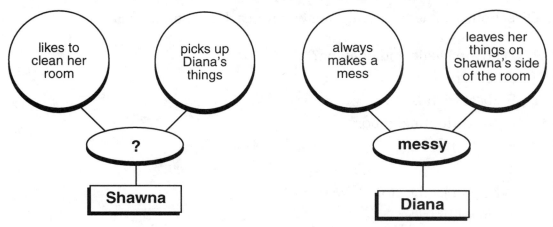

A. neat

B. sloppy

C. tricky

D. mean

Additional Practice Questions

Directions: Now try answering some other kinds of questions about the reading passage. Circle the correct answer for each question.

7. Who is telling this story?
   A. Diana
   B. Shawna
   C. the girls' mother
   D. a narrator who is not in the story

8. What is *most likely* to happen next in the story?
   A. The girls will start to fight.
   B. The girls will take down the wall.
   C. The girls will start to like all of the same things.
   D. The girls will get separate bedrooms.

9. If you were going to retell this story, which of the following would be the *most* important to remember?
   A. The wall that the girls built only stayed up for a few days.
   B. The girls used tape to put a line across the middle of the room.
   C. Diana didn't like Shawna picking up her things when she left them lying around.
   D. The girls discovered that they wanted to be together and learn to get along.

© 1997 Profiles Corporation. DO NOT DUPLICATE.

Lesson 4

The Plot Holds It All Together

A story doesn't really get going until something happens. The "something happens" part is called the **plot**.

A thief can *plot* a robbery. A general can *plot* to take over the government. A girl can *plot* to convince her parents that she needs a puppy. In each case, the *plot* involves both planning and action.

Plot Tips

Following are some tips to help you understand the plot of a story.

Tip 1   Start by finding the main idea.

When a writer comes up with a plot, he or she has a plan in mind. This plan can be stated as a main idea. For example, the sentence below could have been the plan for the story about a certain famous superhero.

> A baby from a doomed planet grows up on Earth, finds out that he has superpowers, and uses them to help people.

Did you recognize this as the plan for the story of Superman?

© 1997 Profiles Corporation. DO NOT DUPLICATE.

Find the problems in a story.

Good stories don't have to be about superheroes. And the action in them doesn't have to involve saving the earth to make them interesting. Even the lives of ordinary families can be the subject of exciting stories—if they're well told. The plot, which includes the problems the characters face, makes all the difference.

Read the following passage from *Ramona and Her Father* by Beverly Cleary.

> Mrs. Quimby looked at the cold creamed cauliflower with distaste, returned it to the refrigerator, and reached for a can of green beans before she noticed her silent and worried daughters watching her for clues as to what might be wrong.
> Mrs. Quimby turned and faced Beezus and Ramona. "Girls, you might as well know. Your father has lost his job."

1. What is the *main* problem in the passage?
    A. The girls' father has lost his job.
    B. The creamed cauliflower is cold.
    C. The refrigerator needs cleaning.
    D. The girls are silent.

Tip 3 **Use what you know about the characters to predict what will happen in the plot.**

The problems in a story create excitement as you anxiously wait to see how the characters will solve them. If you know the characters well, you may be able to predict what will happen next. If the main character is a smart detective caught in a dangerous situation, chances are she'll find a way out.

When making a prediction, don't make wild guesses. Base your answer on what you already know from the passage. A story may have a surprise ending, but you can expect the characters to be true to themselves as their actions take you there.

Here's an example. If a good guy seems to be holding up a bank, in a few pages you know you'll find out that he's doing it for a good reason—like catching a crook. On the other hand, if a bad guy starts handing out diamonds, you can bet he's up to no good.

© 1997 Profiles Corporation. DO NOT DUPLICATE.

Decide who is involved in the problem.

The main character will face problems. That's just the way it goes. Sometimes the problem will be with another character, like a pesky elf, a stern teacher, or a snarling dog. Sometimes the problem will be with a thing, like a broken invention or a difficult test. And sometimes the problem will be with himself— should he tell his parents that he disobeyed them or be quiet and hope they don't find out?

Read the following sentences from *The One in the Middle is the Green Kangaroo* by Judy Blume. The story tells about a boy who has an older brother and a younger sister.

> Freddy thought a lot about being the one in the middle. But there was nothing he could do about it. He felt like the peanut butter part of a sandwich, squeezed between Mike and Ellen.

2. What is Freddy's problem?
   A. His brother and sister are squeezing him too hard.
   B. He doesn't want to eat his peanut butter sandwich.
   C. He doesn't like being the middle child in his family.
   D. He doesn't like his brother and sister.

3. Freddy's problem is with which of the following?
   A. his own feelings
   B. his sister Ellen
   C. his brother Mike
   D. his parents

© 1997 Profiles Corporation. DO NOT DUPLICATE.

Practice Passage

Directions: Read the passage below and answer the questions.

From

Greta and the
Sea Monster

by Hans Janssen

The village of Trog was located at the end of a deep, narrow channel of water that flowed into steep, rocky mountains. The only way out of Trog was to travel by ship down the narrow channel to the distant sea. Once a ship reached the sea, its sailors could travel anywhere in the world. At least that was what the old people of Trog said. For 100 years, the people of the village had been held captive by a sea monster who lived in the channel. No one alive in the village had ever been anywhere but Trog.

There were stories about sailors who had tried to pass the great monster, who was said to have the head of a dragon, the arms of an octopus, and the body of giant snake. The stories all ended the same way. The monster, whose name was Brok, would wrap his many long arms around the ship, then tear it to pieces with his great teeth and jaws. If he happened to swallow a sailor, he

© 1997 Profiles Corporation. DO NOT DUPLICATE.

would spit him out in disgust and say, "I would eat you, too, worm, if you did not taste so bad. Go back to your people before I change my mind."

At some time—no one remembered exactly when—the villagers of Trog stopped trying to leave. No one had seen Brok for many years, but they felt certain he still waited in the cold waters of the channel. How did they know? Because no one from the outside world had visited Trog in 100 years. If there was no way in, the villagers said, there was no way out.

In spite of this, the people were not unhappy. They had made a comfortable life for themselves. They fished from the channel. They cared for their dairy cows, who fed on the steep grassy slopes of the mountains. They grew vegetables during the short mountain summers. There was always plenty to eat and plenty to do.

That was certainly true for Greta, a nine-year-old girl who lived in a tall yellow house on the edge of the water. Greta was as happy as any young girl anywhere. When she was not helping her mother and father with chores, she played games with her friends and went swimming near the docks.

It was well known in the village that no one could swim like Greta. Sometimes people would tease her, in a friendly way. "Greta," they would say, "lift up your chin and smile, so we can see your gills."

One warm Thursday afternoon in July, Greta was swimming with her friends when a dark shape passed near them in the water.

"It's Brok!" one of the girls screamed.

"Don't be silly," Greta said. She was excited herself, but for a different reason. "I saw it. I think it was a seal!"

"A seal?" her friend Inga said. "Seals never travel this far up the channel. No one has ever seen a seal, except in drawings and wood carvings."

"I know what a seal looks like," Greta said. She had only been half listening to her friend. She stared out across the water, hoping to see it again.

A moment later, a brown whiskered face popped from the water, not more than a dozen feet away. The seal seemed to be as interested in Greta as Greta was in it. Then he rolled and swam, heading back down the channel to the sea.

"Look at how he swims!" Greta said, amazed. Without thinking, she rolled in the water, like the seal, and swam after him. Before she knew it, she was far down the channel, away from the fishing boats and tall houses. As good a swimmer as she was, she was not a seal. She could not keep up

EXAMINATION COPY
DO NOT DUPLICATE
©BUCKLE DOWN PUBLISHING CO.

© 1997 Profiles Corporation. DO NOT DUPLICATE.

with him. It was not until she lost sight of the beautiful, graceful beast that she finally heard the people on the shore screaming at her. "Greta! Greta! Have you lost your mind? Brok will eat you for supper!"

Later when her parents heard what she had done, they were glad she was safe, but they were also angry with her. They were so angry, they told her she would spend three days in her room.

Three days is a long time to spend in one place, especially if you are nine. Greta didn't like being trapped in her room. She wanted to be out playing with her friends. More than anything, she wanted to see the seal again. Then she realized she might *never* in her life see a seal again. She and everyone else in Trog were trapped, forever. But why? She knew why she was stuck in her room. But why was Brok keeping them trapped in Trog? That is, if Brok was even still there.

When her mother brought her dinner on the second night, Greta said, "Mother, why does Brok keep us prisoner?"

"What do you mean?" her mother asked.

"I mean, has anyone ever asked Brok why he's doing this?" Greta said. "What does he want?"

"You don't ask monsters questions," her mother said.

If there even is a monster, Greta thought. She knew there was a sea, and a world beyond Trog. But did anyone really know anymore if there was a monster? On the third day, she decided she was going to find out. ❖❖

Sample Plot Questions

Directions: Circle the correct answer to each question.

1. What is the *main* problem in the story?
   A. A seal swims up a channel and scares some children who are swimming.
   B. The people cannot ever leave their village because of a sea monster.
   C. A young girl has to spend three days in her room for swimming with her friends.
   D. A young girl's friends don't like her plans to swim down the channel.

2. What is Greta's *main* problem?
   A. Her parents never let her go outside.
   B. She tries to catch a seal, but he gets away.
   C. She wants to know if there is still a monster in the channel.
   D. Her friends won't swim as far into the channel as she will.

© 1997 Profiles Corporation. DO NOT DUPLICATE.

3. What will *probably* happen next in the story?
    A. Greta will make plans to travel down the channel.
    B. The sea monster will come to the village looking for Greta.
    C. The villagers will send a ship in search of the monster.
    D. Greta will forget all about seeing the seal.

4. What is the *main* reason Greta wants to find out if Brok still lives in the channel?
    A. She wants to go swimming again with her friends.
    B. She wants to see what Brok looks like.
    C. She hopes more seals will visit the village.
    D. She wants to see the rest of the world someday.

Additional Practice Questions

Directions: Now try answering some other kinds of questions about the reading passage. Circle the correct answer to each question.

5. What do we know from the story about the village of Trog?
    A. It is a place where monsters live.
    B. The people who live there are happy.
    C. It is a very large city with many tourists.
    D. It is a town full of very sad people.

6. How is Greta *probably* different from *most* people in the village?
    A. She gets into trouble with her friends.
    B. She likes to find out things for herself.
    C. She doesn't believe there ever was a monster.
    D. She has learned how to swim.

7. Why don't the villagers of Trog travel to other places by land?
    A. They cannot climb over the mountains.
    B. They are too far from other places to walk.
    C. They are surrounded on all sides by water.
    D. They don't believe there is a world beyond Trog.

© 1997 Profiles Corporation. DO NOT DUPLICATE.

8. Why do the people in Greta's village think that the monster is still in the channel?
   A. Greta and her friends see him while swimming.
   B. The monster is still attacking the villagers' ships.
   C. No ships have come to the village from the outside world.
   D. They have never seen seals in the channel.

9. Why do Greta's parents make her stay in her room?
   A. They are upset that she placed herself in danger.
   B. They are trying to hide her from the sea monster.
   C. They want her to think of a plan to get out of the village.
   D. They do not want her to swim with her friends anymore.

10. Why is Greta worried that she may never see a seal again?
    A. She wants the seal to teach her how to swim better.
    B. She thinks no one will believe she really saw a seal.
    C. She realizes that she could be trapped in the village forever.
    D. She is afraid the seal will be eaten by the sea monster.

11. Which word *best* describes Greta at the end of the passage?
    A. angry
    B. quiet
    C. happy
    D. curious

12. Which of the following statements is an opinion?
    A. "No one alive in the village had ever been anywhere but Trog."
    B. "Greta was as happy as any young girl anywhere."
    C. ". . . Greta was swimming with her friends when a dark shape passed near them in the water."
    D. "There were stories about sailors who had tried to pass the great monster . . ."

© 1997 Profiles Corporation. DO NOT DUPLICATE.

Who's Telling This Story?

Every story is told by a **narrator**. Sometimes the narrator will be one of the characters in the story. This is called the **first-person** point of view. Other times the narrator will watch the events happen from outside the story. We call this the **third-person** point of view. In order to understand a story, it is important for you to know who is telling it.

Point-of-View Tips

Following are some tips to help you identify point of view.

Tip 1   **A first-person narrator uses words like "I," "me," "we," and "our." A third-person narrator does not.**

When a story is written in first person, the writer lets one of the characters speak directly to the reader. A first-person narrator is usually easy to recognize. He or she will talk directly to the reader using words like "I" and "me."

1. Read the following sentences from *Otherwise Known As Sheila the Great* by Judy Blume. Circle the words that show the reader that this story has a first-person narrator.

    Today was so hot! My clothes stuck to me and my brain felt all tired out.

When a story is told in **third person**, the narrator is not a part of the story. A third-person narrator describes the other characters and never mentions himself or herself. Third-person narrators never use words like "I" or "me" unless they are reporting what someone else said.

Read the following paragraph from *Homer Price* by Robert McCloskey.

    About two miles outside of Centerburg, where route 56 meets route 56A, there lives a boy named Homer. Homer's father owns a tourist camp. Homer's mother cooks fried chicken and hamburgers in the lunchroom and takes care of the tourist cabins while his father takes care of the filling station. Homer does odd jobs about the place.

© 1997 Profiles Corporation. DO NOT DUPLICATE.

2. Is *Homer Price* written in first-person or third-person point of view?

_____

3. Who is telling the story?
   A. Homer
   B. Homer's father
   C. Homer's mother
   D. a narrator who is not part of the story

 Tip 2   **A first-person narrator may introduce himself or herself to you.**

Sometimes a first-person narrator will introduce himself or herself as the story begins. The following paragraph from *Dancing Carl* by Gary Paulsen is a good example of this.

> It isn't that McKinley is big, or busy. It's only got twelve hundred people—not much more than when my great-grandfather Marshall Knuteson homesteaded the town site. I was named after him and everybody calls me Marsh except Willy who is my best friend and always just says *hey* when he wants me.

4. Who is telling the story?
   A. a boy named Marsh
   B. a boy named Willy
   C. an old man named Marshall
   D. a narrator who is not part of the story

 Tip 3   **"Listen in" on characters' conversations to find out the first-person narrator's name.**

Narrators don't always politely introduce themselves. Sometimes a reader has to look for clues. A good way to do this is to "listen" to conversations between the narrator and the other characters.

Look for the name of the narrator in the following sentences from *Dog Days* by Bernice Myers.

> I dialed Danny's number. His mother answered. "I'm sorry, Benjie, but he's out walking his dog."

© 1997 Profiles Corporation. DO NOT DUPLICATE.

5. Who is the narrator of the story?
   A. Danny
   B. Benjie
   C. Danny's mother
   D. a narrator who is not part of the story

Tip 4 **A first-person narrator doesn't have to be a human.**

This may sound strange, but it's true. Not every first-person story is told through the eyes of a person. A first-person narrator may be a dog, a cow, the moon, or even a pebble. Read the sentences below and answer the questions that follow.

How many more stinky feet will I have to put up with? Every time I start to feel comfy on my royal pillow, more women come along and demand to try me on. Can't they see that their feet are too big for me? I'm just a tiny, delicate glass slipper, after all. The prince had better find Cinderella soon before I crack under all this pressure.

6. Is first-person or third-person point of view used in this story?

   _____

7. Who is telling the story?

   _____

8. How do you know?

   _____

© 1997 Profiles Corporation. DO NOT DUPLICATE.

Practice Passage

Directions: Read the poem below and answer the questions that follow.

Victory

by Jordan Ratliff

Today I race the wind
for the championship of the world.
"On your mark!" I cry.
"Get set!" he warns.
"Go!" I shout
and push off
from the maple tree
at the bottom
of Hanover Hill.
My start's too late,
the wind does not play fair.
But I am speed and power,
streaking through the empty parking lot.
Painted lines blur beneath my skates.
Today I'm faster than the breeze
that chases after me.
Long brown hair ripples
in my wake,
a banner of victory taunting
the slowpoke clouds.

Sample Point of View Question

Directions: Circle the correct answer for the question below.

1. What point of view is used in this poem?
    A. first person, the wind
    B. first person, a skater
    C. third person, the clouds
    D. third person, a narrator who is not part of the story

© 1997 Profiles Corporation. DO NOT DUPLICATE.

Additional Practice Questions

Directions: Now try answering some other kinds of questions about the reading passage. Circle the correct answer for each question.

2. Which sentence *best* tells about the poem?
    A. The speaker is running a race against another person.
    B. The speaker is trying to skate faster than the wind blows.
    C. The speaker is trying to make the wind blow faster.
    D. The speaker is chasing the wind across a parking lot.

3. In the poem, the speaker says, "The wind does not play fair." What does this *most likely* mean?
    A. The wind starts blowing before the speaker shouts "Go!"
    B. The wind doesn't know the rules of the contest.
    C. The wind tries to push the speaker over.
    D. The wind tries to harm the speaker.

4. What are the "painted lines" that "blur" beneath the speaker's skates?
    A. shadows of the tree limbs on the parking lot
    B. cracks in the sidewalk next to the parking lot
    C. designs on the rollers of the speaker's skates
    D. lines that mark the spaces where cars can park

5. What is the meaning of the word "taunting" in the second-to-last line of the poem?
    A. blowing   C. teasing
    B. pulling   D. tying up

6. Which words *best* tell what the wind is like on the day of the race?
    A. quiet and cold   C. swirling and wild
    B. mild and gentle   D. scary and mean

7. Which technique of the author makes the wind seem *most* like a person in the poem?
    A. She tells how hard the wind is blowing.
    B. She causes the wind to lose the race.
    C. She describes the clouds as "slowpoke."
    D. She has the wind speak.

© 1997 Profiles Corporation. DO NOT DUPLICATE.

Unit 2 **Review**

Directions: Read the passage below and answer the questions that follow.

From

CAT WALK

by Mary Stolz

Tootsy-Wootsy knew to the minute when it was his suppertime.
It was suppertime *now*.

Only there was no kitchen, no bowl with CAT written at the bottom. No little girl to wait on him. In his memory, Missy was now all kindness and love. Everything had been done out of love for him. Dressing him up, trundling him about in that doll buggy, trapping him in that yellow sack that prevented him from escaping when all the other animals were free . . .

Free!

He had been walking for a long time, and now it was full dark and he was hungry and still wearing the ski suit that was too tight, and the helmet, and the one front bootie that he could not get off.

But he was a free cat.

His spirits shifted upward. Ahead was a house, with yellow lights at the windows and the familiar sound of a dog's barking.

He was missing Juniper more acutely with each passing moment. Missing the shaggy coat, the doggy smell, the warm talky

companionship of his good, his true, his only friend. No dog would ever take Juniper's place for him, but any dog was better than no dog at all to be close to.

© 1997 Profiles Corporation. DO NOT DUPLICATE.

This one had a voice that boomed like a storm in the hills, where Juniper's bark was more like bells, but a bark was a bark and meant dog, and Tootsy-Wootsy confidently ran toward it.

The next thing he knew, and he didn't remember getting there, he was clutching a tree branch while down below—not far enough down—this terrible huge animal was roaring and trying to knock the tree over.

From the house, a woman started calling to him, telling him to stop that racket, but the creature paid no attention. Just kept bounding and bellowing. Tootsy-Wootsy, faint with fear, with hunger, with cold, with wild regret for all he'd left behind him, dug in his claws and waited—for what, he knew not.

The woman, pulling on a sweater, came out of the house and made the dog, whose awful name was Soldier, be quiet.

"Stay!" she said to him. "Sit! What *is* up there in the tree?"

The monster sat, staring upward, tongue lolling, and the woman went away. Then she came back, with a man. Then a blinding light forced Tootsy-Wootsy to close his eyes.

He could not think. All memory of Juniper, the kitchen, his bowl with CAT on the bottom and chicken on top, disappeared. He was a small bundle of terror in pink and purple, treed by a superdog, trapped in torchlight.

He gave up hope.

At the bottom of the tree the man, the woman, and the dog were all looking up.

"At first I thought it was a *baby*," said the woman.

"How would a baby get up in our beech tree?"

"Why would a cat be dressed in ski clothes?"

"How should I know? The latest cat fad, maybe." ❖❖

EXAMINATION COPY
DO NOT DUPLICATE
©BUCKLE DOWN PUBLISHING CO.

© 1997 Profiles Corporation. DO NOT DUPLICATE.

Unit 2 Review Questions

Directions: Circle the correct answer for each question.

1. What time of day does the story take place?
   A. morning
   B. afternoon
   C. night
   D. midday

2. Who is Tootsy-Wootsy?
   A. a cat
   B. a dog
   C. a baby
   D. a little girl

3. Who is telling this story?
   A. Tootsy-Wootsy
   B. Missy
   C. Soldier
   D. a narrator who is not part of the story

4. Which answer best completes the graphic organizer?

Similarities and Differences

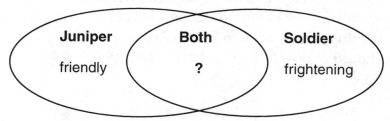

   A. climbing
   B. roaring
   C. licking
   D. barking

© 1997 Profiles Corporation. DO NOT DUPLICATE.

5. What is Tootsy-Wootsy's *main* problem?
   A. He misses his friend Juniper.
   B. He can't take off the ski suit.
   C. He's trapped in a tree with a dog below him.
   D. It is suppertime and he is hungry.

6. How does Tootsy-Wootsy feel about Soldier at the end of the story?
   A. frightened of him
   B. comforted by him
   C. happy to see him
   D. bored by him

7. What is *most likely* to happen next in the story?
   A. The man and woman will walk away and leave Tootsy-Wootsy alone with Soldier.
   B. The man and woman will get Tootsy-Wootsy safely down from the tree.
   C. Tootsy-Wootsy will come down from the tree and make friends with Soldier.
   D. Soldier will knock the tree down and get Tootsy-Wootsy.

8. Why is "Soldier" a good name for the woman's dog?
   A. He guards the woman's home.
   B. He gets into many fights.
   C. He is very loud for a dog.
   D. He is not very friendly.

© 1997 Profiles Corporation. DO NOT DUPLICATE.

Additional Practice Questions

Directions: Now try answering some other types of questions about the reading passage.

9. Why is Tootsy-Wootsy dressed in a ski suit?
   A. He likes wearing baby clothes.
   B. A girl put the clothes on him.
   C. He put it on to stay warm on his walk.
   D. It is the latest fad for cats.

10. What good thing has happened to Tootsy-Wootsy at the start of the passage?
    A. He was dressed up in ski clothes.
    B. There is food in his supper dish.
    C. He has had a ride in a doll buggy.
    D. He has gained his freedom.

11. What do the words "His spirits shifted upward" mean?
    A. Tootsy-Wootsy started to feel more hopeful.
    B. Tootsy-Wootsy climbed higher in the tree.
    C. Tootsy-Wootsy looked up at the tree.
    D. Tootsy-Wootsy began to think about Missy.

12. What is the source of the "blinding light" that forces Tootsy-Wootsy to close his eyes?
    A. the sun
    B. a flashlight
    C. a candle
    D. a fire

© 1997 Profiles Corporation. DO NOT DUPLICATE.

Going Deeper into the Passage

Lesson 6

Making Comparisons

Comparisons show how things, characters, settings, or events are alike and different. Making a comparison involves looking for things that are *different* as well as *alike*.

The following passage shows similarities and differences in the way a boy named Henry and his dog Ribsy walk home after school during the week. It is from *Henry Huggins* by Beverly Cleary.

> Every afternoon after school Ribsy waited for Henry under a fir tree in the corner of the school yard. Four days a week they ran home the shortest way, past the park, up the hill, and through the vacant lot.
> On Fridays, however, they walked home the long way round past the Rose City Drugstore, the Supermarket, the Ideal Barber Shop, and the Lucky Dog Pet Shop.

1. What was different about the way Henry and Ribsy walked home on Fridays?
   A. They went through a vacant lot.
   B. They went past the park.
   C. They took a longer path.
   D. They met under a fir tree.

© 1997 Profiles Corporation. DO NOT DUPLICATE.

2. How was the walk home on Fridays the same as the walk home on the other days of the week?

    A. They walked home together.

    B. They always stopped at the Lucky Dog Pet Shop.

    C. They went home as fast as they could.

    D. They walked past the Supermarket.

Comparison Tips

Following are tips to help you make comparisons.

 Look for word clues that tell when things are being compared.

The lists below contain some words and phrases (groups of words). These are clues that tell you that the writer is making a comparison.

Similarities	Differences
alike	but
both	however
just as	instead of
similar	not the same as
the same as	on the other hand

3. Read the following passage from *The Amazing Bo Jackson* by Randi Hacker. It tells about pro athlete Bo Jackson's early baseball career. As you read, underline the clue words that show a comparison.

    Bo's life in the minor leagues wasn't as glamorous as it might have been if he had decided to play pro football. Instead of riding in limousines and eating expensive food, he found himself riding for 15 hours in a bus and eating greasy hamburgers.

4. How did Bo's life as a minor league baseball player compare to what it would have been like as a pro football player?

    A. He was treated more like an ordinary person.

    B. He didn't get to eat as much food as he wanted.

    C. He had to travel farther than a football player.

    D. He was able to purchase a bus to travel in.

© 1997 Profiles Corporation. DO NOT DUPLICATE.

Look for words that give direct comparisons, like "bigger," "smallest," "more," and "less."

Words that show a direct comparison are often the easiest to recognize. They also help you to know how many things are being compared. Comparison words ending in "er" compare only two things. Comparison words ending in "est" compare three or more things.

The passage below is from *Dogsong* by Gary Paulsen. It describes two kinds of ice found in Alaska.

5. Circle the comparison words in the passage. Then underline any other clue words that tell you a comparison is being made.

> Sea ice is not the same as fresh-water ice. The salt-water ice is stronger, more elastic, isn't as slippery. Also the sea ice moves all the time, even when it is thick.

6. What two things are being compared in the passage?

   _____

   _____

Notice that sea ice is also called "salt-water ice" in the passage. The author tells four ways that sea ice (salt-water ice) is different from fresh-water ice. Fill in the blanks to finish the comparisons below.

7. Sea ice is _____ than fresh-water ice.

8. Sea ice is _____ than fresh-water ice.

9. Sea ice is not as _____ as fresh-water ice.

10. Fresh-water ice doesn't _____ all the time like sea ice does.

© 1997 Profiles Corporation. DO NOT DUPLICATE.

If there are no clue words, look for details that show comparisons.

Some comparisons are made just by giving detailed descriptions. The following passage from *Kevin's Grandma* by Barbara Williams does this. In the story, Kevin is the narrator's friend.

> On my birthday my grandma takes me out to lunch. Then we go shopping. She buys me any toy I want.
>
> On Kevin's birthday his grandma takes him in an airplane. He watches from the window while she goes skydiving.

11. Who is being compared in this story?
    A. the narrator and his grandma
    B. the narrator and Kevin's grandma
    C. Kevin's grandma and the narrator's grandma
    D. Kevin and his grandma

12. On their birthdays, what do Kevin and the narrator do alike?
    A. spend the day with their grandmothers
    B. fly in an airplane
    C. go shopping for a new toy
    D. go out to lunch

 Draw a chart to show similarities and differences.

A chart can help you to organize information so that comparisons are easier to make. Read the following information about pro wrestler Andre the Giant. It is from *Kings of the Ring: An Inside Guide to Pro Wrestling* by Joe Bosko.

> *Everything* about Andre is BIG. His fingers are so large that you could slip a silver dollar through one of his rings. By comparison, William "The Refrigerator" Perry's* fingers are tiny—you can only fit a half dollar through one of his rings. Andre's wrist is almost twelve inches around. That's an average-size wrist—for a gorilla. Most human wrists are about seven inches around.

*William Perry was a pro football player whose very large size earned him the nickname "The Refrigerator."

© 1997 Profiles Corporation. DO NOT DUPLICATE.

13. Finish filling in the unshaded parts of the chart with information from the passage.

How Andre the Giant Compares to Others

Name	Finger Size	Wrist Size
Andre the Giant	Wears a ring large enough to fit a silver dollar through	12 inches around
William "The Refrigerator" Perry		
Gorilla		
Average Human		

14. Whose finger size would *most likely* be the *smallest*?
    A. Andre the Giant
    B. an average human
    C. a gorilla
    D. William Perry

15. How does Andre's wrist compare to that of an average gorilla?
    A. It is slightly larger.
    B. It is slightly smaller.
    C. It is about half the size.
    D. It is about the same size.

© 1997 Profiles Corporation. DO NOT DUPLICATE.

Practice Passage

Directions: Read the passage below to learn more about comparison questions. As you read, circle words in the passage that show a comparison.

No Place Like Home

by Angela Roney

Do you know the story of *The Wizard of Oz*? In the story, a little girl named Dorothy is reminded that "There's no place like home." When it comes to planets, there really *is* no place like home. No other planet is quite like our planet Earth.

Earth is one of the nine planets that travel around the star we call the Sun. The other planets in our solar system[1] are Mercury, Venus, Mars, Jupiter, Saturn, Uranus, Neptune, and Pluto. Earth has many things in common with the other planets. But there are also ways in which Earth is very different.

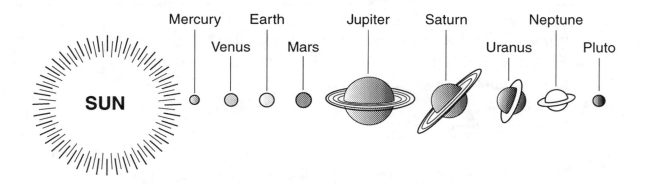

Earth is the fifth largest planet in our solar system. Jupiter, the largest planet, is about 11 times the size of Earth. The smallest planet is Pluto. It is less than one-fifth the size of our planet.

Like the other planets, Earth is constantly moving. It travels around the Sun, taking a little over 365 days (one year) to make the trip. Pluto takes the longest—almost 250 years. Mercury, the speediest planet, takes only 88 days to go around the Sun.

As it is traveling, Earth is also spinning like a top. It spins on an imaginary line that connects the North and South poles through Earth's center. (This line is called the Earth's *axis*.) Earth makes one full spin in about 24 hours, or one day.

[1]A solar system is made up of a star and all the planets and other objects that travel around it.

© 1997 Profiles Corporation. DO NOT DUPLICATE.

Besides traveling around the Sun and spinning on its axis, Earth is also moving with the Sun and the rest of our solar system through our galaxy.[2] We call our galaxy the Milky Way.

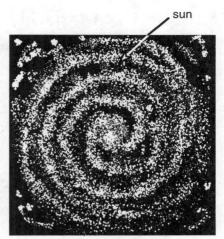

sun

The Milky Way

Like Pluto, Earth has only one moon. A moon travels around a planet in much the same way that a planet travels around the Sun. Our moon is about one-fourth the size of Earth. Mercury and Venus have no moons at all. The rest of the planets have two or more moons. Saturn has the most, a whopping 18 moons!

Four planets have something the Earth doesn't: rings. Jupiter, Saturn, Uranus, and Neptune are circled by colorful rings. Most rings are either made up of ice particles or of floating dust particles that circle the planet.

Earth is the only planet in our solar system with enough oxygen to support large life forms. About two-thirds of Earth's surface is covered with water, an important ingredient for life. Air, water, and just the right temperature make possible all the amazing plants and animals you see here.

Scientists have always doubted that life exists on other planets. Now they may be changing their minds. They have recently found evidence of possible life on Mars. Fossils from that planet show that tiny life forms may have existed there billions of years ago. Mars has a very small amount of water and oxygen, but it gets much colder there than on Earth. The forms of life on our planet could not exist on Mars.

Conditions on other planets may be able to support some tiny kinds of living creatures. However, the living things on Earth are truly unique. You can look around at Earth's wildlife—and even at yourself—and know that there is truly no place like home. Well, as far as we know . . .

© 1997 Profiles Corporation. DO NOT DUPLICATE.

[2]A galaxy is a group of billions of stars. Each galaxy has many solar systems in it.

Sample Comparison Questions

Directions: Circle the correct answer for each question.

1. Which of the following moves *most* like Earth turns on its axis?
   A. a basketball spinning on someone's fingertip
   B. a roller coaster going downhill
   C. clothes drying in a clothes dryer
   D. a train traveling down a track

2. What is one way in which Earth is like all the other planets in our solar system?
   A. It is surrounded by rings.
   B. It has only one moon.
   C. It is always moving.
   D. It has large life forms.

3. What do Jupiter, Saturn, Uranus, and Neptune have in common?
   A. They are all smaller than Earth.
   B. They each have 18 moons.
   C. They are closer to the Sun than Earth.
   D. They each have rings around them.

4. Which planet is *largest*?
   A. Earth
   B. Jupiter
   C. Neptune
   D. Pluto

5. The way that a moon travels around a planet is *most* like which of the following?
   A. the way that Venus travels around the Sun
   B. the way that a rocket travels to the Earth's moon
   C. the way that heat travels from the Sun
   D. the way that the Earth spins on its axis

© 1997 Profiles Corporation. DO NOT DUPLICATE.

6. Which answer *best* completes the graphic organizer?

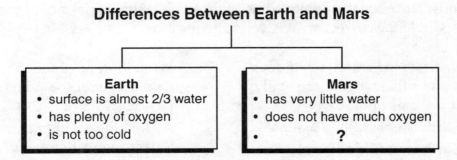

Differences Between Earth and Mars

Earth
- surface is almost 2/3 water
- has plenty of oxygen
- is not too cold

Mars
- has very little water
- does not have much oxygen
- **?**

A. doesn't travel around the sun

B. temperature gets very cold

C. has never had any life forms

D. has large plants and animals

EXAMINATION COPY
DO NOT DUPLICATE
©BUCKLE DOWN PUBLISHING CO.

© 1997 Profiles Corporation. DO NOT DUPLICATE.

Additional Practice Questions

Directions: Now try answering some other kinds of questions about the reading passage. Circle the correct answer for each question.

7. In the first paragraph, what does the author mean by "there really *is* no place like home"?
   A. Earth is not really a planet.
   B. Earth is unlike other planets in many ways.
   C. Other planets are not interesting.
   D. People will never be able to leave Earth.

8. What is the *best* strategy to use in answering question #7?
   A. Carefully reread the first paragraph of the passage.
   B. Scan the rest of the passage for the word *home*.
   C. Reread the entire passage carefully.
   D. Make a chart showing ways that Earth is different from other planets.

9. What would be the *best* way to check to see if the information in this passage is correct?
   A. Read a biography of a famous astronaut.
   B. Look up *planets* in an encyclopedia.
   C. Watch a movie about people traveling in space.
   D. Reread the passage.

10. What kind of experience would help you *most* to understand this passage?
    A. looking at other planets through a telescope
    B. playing with a set of *Star Wars* action figures
    C. reading a science fiction story about Martians
    D. watching the landing of a space shuttle on television

11. How does the illustration of the planets help you understand the article?
    A. It shows what each planet in the solar system is made of.
    B. It shows why scientists doubt that life exists on other planets.
    C. It shows how long it takes each planet to travel around the Sun.
    D. It shows how the planets compare in size and in distance from the Sun.

12. The author makes the article easy to understand by doing all of the following *except* which one?
    A. by giving definitions of difficult terms in footnotes
    B. by giving illustrations of the planets and the galaxy
    C. by giving details about several of the planets
    D. by giving details about many of the life forms on Earth

© 1997 Profiles Corporation. DO NOT DUPLICATE.

Lesson 7

What's the Problem?

Most fiction passages (made-up stories) have at least one **problem**. Sometimes a story will have a main problem and a few less important problems. The problems are almost always solved by the end of the story. The way in which a problem is solved is called the **solution**.

A nonfiction passage (about real things) may also have one or more problems and solutions. Identifying both the problems and the solutions is an important part of understanding what you read.

Practice Passage

Directions: Read the following passage to learn more about problems and solutions.

Dilly Comes to Dinner

by Paul Highland

"Good grief, Samarra! What's *that*?" her father asked. On the table next to Samarra's plate was a rather large, very plump toad.

"Ribbitt," the toad croaked.

Samarra giggled. "It's just my toad, Dad. His name's Dilly because his skin is green and bumpy like a pickle. I found him in the alley today. He looked hungry, so I decided to give him something to eat."

"Not at our dinner table, you're not," her father said.

"Your dad's right," her mom said as she dished up the mashed potatoes. "I think you'd better put Dilly somewhere a little safer. Somebody might get a taste for a pickle and take a bite out of him." She laughed at her own joke. Samarra and Dad just groaned. Mom was always trying to make jokes that weren't funny.

Samarra reached out her hands to pick up her new pet. But Dilly was too fast. He jumped over her right arm and landed in the salad.

"YUCK!" her father said.

"Oh, for heaven's sake!" her mother said.

"Dilly!" Samarra cried. She leaned over the table and grabbed the salad bowl. "Got you now!"

© 1997 Profiles Corporation. DO NOT DUPLICATE.

But once again Dilly was too quick. He hopped out of the salad and into the mashed potatoes. They must have been too hot, because he didn't stay there long. Next he hopped on top of the fried chicken. It was too hot, too. With a powerful leap, he landed in the lemonade pitcher.

Quickly Dad picked up the pitcher and carried it to the sink. He poured out the lemonade and carefully held Dilly under the faucet to rinse him off.

Mom and Samarra looked at the salad. They looked at the mashed potatoes. They looked at Dad as he walked to the kitchen door and put the freshly washed Dilly outside. Then everybody looked at each other.

"I suddenly have a craving for pizza," Mom said.

This time they all laughed. ❖❖

Problem and Solution Tips

Following are tips to help you answer questions about the story you just read.

 Tip 1 **First determine the main idea.**

The main idea is often the main problem in the story.

1. What's the *main* idea of the passage?
    A. A girl's mother can't tell a funny joke.
    B. A pet toad jumps into a family's dinner.
    C. Samarra names a toad after a pickle.
    D. A family sits down together for dinner.

 Tip 2 **Identify what problem each character faces.**

Sometimes a story has more than one problem. The main character is almost always faced with the biggest problem. Other characters may each face a different problem, or several characters may face the same problem.

2. What is the *main* problem that Samarra faces?
    A. what to feed her pet toad Dilly
    B. how to get permission to keep her toad
    C. how to catch Dilly before he ruins the meal
    D. how to order a new meal

© 1997 Profiles Corporation. DO NOT DUPLICATE.

3. On the lines below, tell what other problems the characters have.

_____

_____

_____

_____

_____

 Look for the cause of the problem. Then try to put it into a "because" sentence.

Finding what caused a problem is important. It can help you understand how a problem started and how it can be solved. The best way to find what caused a problem is usually to connect the problem and its possible cause into a "because" sentence.

An important problem in the story is that a toad is spoiling the family's dinner. Let's trace the problem and find its cause.

What causes the family's dinner to be spoiled?

The family's dinner is spoiled *because* a toad jumps in the food.

Would a dinner be spoiled if a toad jumped in the food? Most people would probably think so.

Let's take one step backward. Fill in the blank to finish the sentence.

4. Why does a toad jump in the food?

A toad jumps in the food *because*

_____

Got the idea? Now try a multiple-choice question. Choose the correct answer.

5. Why does Samarra's father say, "Yuck"?
   A. because he doesn't like the taste of the chicken
   B. because he sees Samarra touch a toad
   C. because he sees a toad hop in the salad
   D. because he does not like frogs

© 1997 Profiles Corporation. DO NOT DUPLICATE.

Tip 4   **Find out how the problem is solved.**

Once you know what the problem is and what caused it, you can look for the solution. Find the solution for each of the following problems in the story.

6. How does the family catch Dilly?
   A. Samarra picks up the salad bowl.
   B. Dad picks up the lemonade pitcher.
   C. Mom picks up the mashed potatoes.
   D. Samarra picks up the fried chicken.

7. How does Dilly get away from the people?
   A. Dad puts him outside of the house.
   B. He hops through the kitchen door.
   C. Samarra puts him back in the alley.
   D. He hops through a window.

8. How does Mom finally make the family laugh?
   A. She says someone might take a bite out of Dilly.
   B. She shows surprise when the toad hops on the table.
   C. She says something when she looks at the spoiled dinner.
   D. She says something when Dilly jumps in the salad bowl.

9. What does the family *most likely* eat for dinner?
   A. pizza
   B. fried chicken
   C. dill pickles
   D. mashed potatoes

© 1997 Profiles Corporation. DO NOT DUPLICATE.

Practice Passage

Directions: Read the passage below to learn more about problem and solution questions.

Virginia Beach, Virginia, lies on a flat stretch of Atlantic Ocean coastline. Like other cities in the United States, Virginia Beach has produced a lot of trash over the years. Tons of it, in fact. And like most other cities, Virginia Beach has buried some of it in dumps, burned some of it, and recycled some of it.

But dumps smell foul and attract rats. Burning causes air pollution. Recycling only works for some types of items. And the trash just keeps coming. For a long time, the city of Virginia Beach had been faced with a common problem—what to do with so much trash. About thirty years ago, the community decided it was time for a new plan.

Some people came up with an exciting idea. Virginia Beach, they said, was flat—maybe too flat. So flat that there were no hills to climb. So flat that no one could get up high enough to look out over the ocean. Why not use the tons of trash to build a mountain?

The city engineers got together and talked about this idea. They did a lot of research to find out whether it would be safe to build a mountain out of trash. Finally, they decided to do it.

For five years, workers piled the trash into layers and covered them with dirt. They packed the dirt down tightly in and around discarded truck tires, broken sofas, orange peelings, rusty swing sets, and all sorts of other junk. They piled layer on top of layer until 64,000 tons of trash were buried under a thick blanket of dirt. The city of Virginia Beach had a mountain at last. Someone nicknamed it "Mount Trashmore."

Today, Mount Trashmore is covered with vegetation. It provides hiking trails and other recreation as well as a habitat for many small animals. People come from all over the world to see how one community turned their trash into a treasure. ❖❖❖

Sample Problem and Solution Questions

Directions: Circle the correct answer for each question.

1. What was Virginia Beach's *main* problem?
   A. The city needed a better way to get rid of tons of trash.
   B. The land was too flat for the people to look out over the ocean.
   C. The people of the city needed a hiking trail and recreation area.
   D. The city officials wanted to find a way to attract more visitors.

2. Why did the city need to do something different with its trash?
   A. because the city needed a place to plant things
   B. because the people wanted to have a mountain
   C. because there are problems with dumping, burning, and recycling
   D. because the city had begun producing less trash than before

3. What *main* problem was caused by burning trash?
   A. Rats got into the ashes after the trash was burned.
   B. The air became polluted from the smoke.
   C. Some things couldn't be burned.
   D. Not enough space was available for burning trash.

4. What solution did Virginia Beach find for its trash problem?
   A. bury the trash in deeper dumps
   B. recycle more kinds of trash
   C. burn more of the trash
   D. make the trash into a mountain

5. What is the *most likely* reason that people come from other parts of the world to see Mount Trashmore?
   A. because they want to look out over the ocean
   B. because they want to see animals that live on a mountain
   C. because it is a good place for hiking and other recreation
   D. because it is an unusual way to handle a city's trash

© 1997 Profiles Corporation. DO NOT DUPLICATE.

Additional Practice Questions

Directions: Now try answering some other kinds of questions about the reading passage. Circle the correct answer for each question.

6. Where is Mount Trashmore located?

    A. near an ocean

    B. in a big mountain range

    C. next to a large lake

    D. in a desert

7. Before Mount Trashmore was started, how many ways did Virginia Beach use to get rid of trash?

    A. 1

    B. 2

    C. 3

    D. 4

8. What was the *first* thing that the city engineers did to build Mount Trashmore?

    A. They packed together a layer of trash.

    B. They studied the idea to see whether it was safe.

    C. They spread out a thick blanket of dirt.

    D. They covered it with plants and trees.

9. The passage says that the community of Virginia Beach "turned their trash into a treasure." How is Mount Trashmore a "treasure"?

    A. It hides many usable items that people have thrown away.

    B. It provides recreation for people and new habitats for animals.

    C. The city charges people money to see Mount Trashmore.

    D. There is treasure buried among the trash.

10. Which of the following would be the *best* title for this passage?

    A. "From Trash to Treasure"

    B. "Dumping Won't Do: How to Recycle Your Trash"

    C. "Guide to the Best Vacation Spots"

    D. "Tales of Lost Treasure"

© 1997 Profiles Corporation. DO NOT DUPLICATE.

11. What is the author's *main* purpose in this passage?
    A. to complain
    B. to entertain
    C. to frighten
    D. to inform

12. *While* you are reading, which of the following would help you *most* to understand the passage?
    A. reading each sentence twice before going on to the next sentence
    B. stopping to retell the main points of each paragraph to make sure you understand the passage
    C. reading the first and last paragraphs to find out the important ideas
    D. stopping to see how many paragraphs you have read so far

13. What conclusion can you draw from the passage?
    A. Cities on the Atlantic Ocean have the most trash.
    B. Trash mountains are the only good places to take vacations.
    C. It only takes a small amount of trash to make a mountain.
    D. Other cities could also make mountains out of trash.

© 1997 Profiles Corporation. DO NOT DUPLICATE.

Unit 3 Review

Directions: Read the passage below and answer the questions that follow.

From

Jennifer Murdley's Toad

by Bruce Coville

If Jennifer Murdley hadn't been forced to wear her brother's underpants to school, the whole thing might never have happened. But when she walked into the laundry room on the morning of October 13th, she found her father pouring liquid detergent onto a load of clothes that included every pair of underwear she owned.

"Dad!" she screamed. "Wait!"

She was too late. The tub was filling, her underwear was soggy and soapy, and there was no chance of getting any of it dry before she had to leave for school.

"Don't worry," said Mr. Murdley, holding up a stack of neatly folded underpants, "you can wear a pair of these!"

"You have got to be kidding! Those belong to Skippy!"

The conversation that followed wasn't pretty. The bottom line had been that Jennifer *was* going to school, and she *was* going to wear underwear, even if it did belong to her brother.

Although she promised Skippy to keep it a secret, Jennifer confided the embarrassing truth to one person—her best friend, Ellen.

Ellen, not unnaturally, thought it was funny.

So she told Annette.

Annette told Maya.

Maya told Sharra.

And Sharra, as could have been expected, told the world.

By recess every boy in the fifth grade knew Jennifer's secret. They chased her around the playground, chanting, "Jennifer Murdley went to France, wearing her brother's underpants," while Sharra and her friends stood in a circle, giggling and pointing.

As if that weren't bad enough, when Jennifer passed Skippy in the hallway later that day, as her class was leaving art and his was entering, he hissed, "You *die*, creepazoid." ❖❖

© 1997 Profiles Corporation. DO NOT DUPLICATE.

Unit 3 Review Questions

Directions: Circle the correct answer for each question.

1. What is Jennifer's *main* problem?
   A. Her brother is mad at her.
   B. She doesn't have any friends.
   C. She has to wear her brother's underpants.
   D. She was late for school.

2. What is the *main* cause of Jennifer's trouble at school?
   A. Her brother goes to her school.
   B. Skippy called her a creepazoid.
   C. Everyone knows her secret.
   D. Her friend Ellen is mean to her.

3. Who *first* causes Jennifer's secret to spread?
   A. Maya
   B. Sharra
   C. Skippy
   D. Jennifer

4. What do Ellen and Maya do alike?
   A. They both chase Jennifer around the playground.
   B. They both tell someone else about Jennifer's underpants.
   C. They both embarrass Jennifer in art class.
   D. They both keep Jennifer's secret.

5. Which answer *best* completes the graphic organizer?

   The Fifth Grade Boys and Sharra and Her Friends

   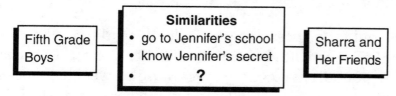

   A. make fun of Jennifer
   B. chase Jennifer around the playground
   C. say a mean rhyme about Jennifer
   D. point their fingers at Jennifer

© 1997 Profiles Corporation. DO NOT DUPLICATE.

Additional Practice Questions

Directions: Now try answering some other types of questions about the reading passage. Circle the correct answer for each question.

6. Who is telling this story?
    A. Jennifer
    B. Skippy
    C. Jennifer's father
    D. a narrator who is not part of the story

7. When the author says, "The bottom line had been . . . ," what does he mean?
    A. "Mr. Murdley's final word had been . . ."
    B. "The lower clothesline had been . . ."
    C. "Jennifer's laundry had been . . ."
    D. "Skippy's response had been . . ."

8. What does the author mean by "The conversation that followed wasn't pretty"?
    A. Jennifer and her father are not good-looking.
    B. Jennifer and her father made ugly faces at each other.
    C. Mr. Murdley and his daughter had an argument.
    D. Skippy's underpants did not look very nice.

9. How did Skippy feel when he found out that the other kids knew Jennifer was wearing his underpants?
    A. pleased that someone else was teasing Jennifer
    B. angry that people knew they were his underpants
    C. bored because it seemed like a silly thing to tease her about
    D. sad because Jennifer's friends didn't keep her secret

10. What do you know about Sharra from this story?
    A. She never keeps secrets.   C. She doesn't have any friends.
    B. She is nice to Jennifer.   D. She is friends with Skippy.

11. What would be a good motto for this passage?
    A. Share and share alike.
    B. A friend in need is a friend indeed.
    C. The early bird gets the worm.
    D. The best kept secret is the one that's never told.

© 1997 Profiles Corporation. DO NOT DUPLICATE.

Understanding the Author's Message

UNIT 4

 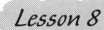

Is That a Fact?

Some people will believe anything they see in print. They think, "If it's nonfiction, it must be a fact." That's not always true. Much of what is written is fact, but some of it is just the writer's opinion.

EXAMINATION COPY
DO NOT DUPLICATE
©BUCKLE DOWN PUBLISHING CO.

 **Tip 1 A statement of fact can be checked out to see if it is correct.**

When someone makes a **fact** statement, they're saying, "This is the truth. Go ahead and check on it."

If your friend Mika says, "My guinea pig Bruiser weighs almost a pound," she's making a statement of fact. You can check to see if her statement is correct by putting Bruiser on a scale.

Of course, Mika might be wrong; Bruiser might actually weigh more than a pound. Even so, Mika's statement isn't her opinion. We know she made a statement of fact because it can be checked out.

 Tip 2 A statement of opinion cannot be checked out to see if it's correct.

If Mika says that Bruiser is "the sweetest little piggie you could ever hope to meet," she's stating her **opinion**. She may think he's the sweetest; you may think he's a monster. Some people will agree with Mika; some will agree with you. Her opinion about Bruiser can't be checked out.

© 1997 Profiles Corporation. DO NOT DUPLICATE.

Tip 3 **Watch for "judgment words" to help you spot an opinion.**

Some words jump right out and tell you that they are an opinion. Here are some examples:

lovely—ugly   cruel—kind

frightening—enjoyable   delicious—disgusting

wonderful—horrible   worst—best

a lot—a little

All of the words listed above express an opinion because they mean different things to different people.

Tip 4 **Fact statements contain words that mean the same thing to everybody.**

Fact statements don't contain judgment words. Instead, they have words with meanings that everyone can agree on. Here are some examples:

red	twenty	round	Canadian
empty	open	plastic	metal
broken	first place	polka-dotted	square

If Mika says, "Bruiser has red fur with a band of white around his neck," she's stating a fact. You can check it out for yourself by looking at Bruiser.

Directions: Read the following sentences. Put an "F" in front of each **Fact** statement. Put an "O" in front of each **Opinion** statement.

_____ 1. The Cape Fear Museum is in Wilmington, North Carolina.

_____ 2. Paramount's Carowinds has the most exciting rides of any amusement park.

_____ 3. The Asheville Public Library has every book in the *Boxcar Children* series.

_____ 4. R.L. Stine writes really scary books.

_____ 5. When I type on a computer keyboard, my fingers make a sound like chickens dancing on the roof.

_____ 6. Snow Skiing in the Appalachian Mountains is really fun.

_____ 7. My family takes a vacation trip to Atlantic Beach every summer.

© 1997 Profiles Corporation. DO NOT DUPLICATE.

_____ 8. The Tar Heels basketball team is the best ever!

_____ 9. Bears live in Nantahala National Forest.

_____ 10. The movie we should watch is *The Hunchback of Notre Dame.*

Now let's take a look at the statements you labeled.

1. Even if you've never been to the Cape Fear Museum, you could still check this out by calling your local library, by calling the state tourism office, or by asking people who have been to Wilmington. This is a statement of **fact**.

2. "Most exciting" are judgment words. To you, the rides at Carowinds may be the most exciting of any rides anywhere. But your best friend may think that they are boring compared to the ones at Six Flags in Atlanta. This is a statement of **opinion**.

3. You can check out this statement. Somewhere there is a list of all the *Boxcar Children* books. All you have to do is check the Asheville Public Library's card catalog to find out whether they have them all. This is a statement of **fact**.

4. R.L. Stine writes books that a lot of people would think are scary. But not everyone may think so. This is a statement of **opinion**.

5. Your fingers might sound like dancing chickens to you; your friend Max may think they sound like elephants stomping. This is a statement of **opinion**.

6. You may like snow skiing, but it might scare your Aunt Myrtle to death. This is a statement of **opinion**.

7. You can check out this statement by asking the family members where they vacation each summer. Even if the person making this statement forgot about going to Washington, D.C., last summer, it is still a statement of **fact** because it can be checked.

8. The Tar Heels have won the national basketball championship four times in the history of the team. But the word "best" might mean different things to different people. Are they the "best" because they win a lot, or because they show good sportsmanship, or because the team members often go on to play for professional teams, or . . . ? The word "best" is a judgment word, so this statement is an **opinion**.

9. This statement can be checked out. You could call the park rangers at the Nantahala National Forest and ask them. This is a statement of **fact**.

10. You may agree or disagree about which movie to watch. This is an **opinion**.

© 1997 Profiles Corporation. DO NOT DUPLICATE.

Practice Passage

Directions: Read the passage below to learn more about fact and opinion questions.

by Harriet Rosenbaum

It sounds like a joke and the cartoon above *is* a joke; however, a zonkey is a real animal. It's a *hybrid*—a mixed breed born from parents of two different types of animals. You already know one famous hybrid—the mule. Mules have been around for thousands of years. Zonkeys, ligers, tiglons, beefaloes, and many others have only recently come to life.

Different kinds of animals do not naturally reproduce together. In the wild, you'd never find a lion and a tiger sharing a home and family. But new scientific methods have made it possible for ligers (a cross between a female tiger and a male lion) and tiglons (a cross between a male tiger and a female lion) to be born.

A hybrid is somewhat like each of its parents. For example, some zonkeys have black and white stripes like a zebra, but only on part of their bodies. The rest of their hide is usually tan like a donkey. Beefaloes may have heads that look like beef cattle and bodies shaped like buffaloes. With most hybrids, it's pretty easy to tell which two animals are the parents just by looking at their offspring.

But why would anyone want to fool with nature to create a new animal?

© 1997 Profiles Corporation. DO NOT DUPLICATE.

Because hybrids often have the best features of both their parents. In some ways they may be even better than either their mother or their father.

A mule (a cross between a male donkey and a female horse) can work harder than either parent. It can also pull more weight and work longer hours.

A yakow (a cross between a yak and a cow) usually gives more milk than either a cow or a yak. It is also likely to be more good-natured than a yak and stronger than either of its parents.

Beefaloes (a cross between beef cattle and buffaloes) don't need to eat corn and other expensive grains like beef cattle do. They can live on grass. And, like their hardy buffalo parents, their powerful legs and strong hooves can break through snow to find food to eat. Their meat is also tastier than buffalo and maybe even better than beef.

If some scientists have their way, the world will soon see many other marvelous hybrids. Although these zonkeys and other hybrids seem unusual today, one day they may all be as common as mules.

Picture this: Ten years from now you drive up to a fast-food restaurant for dinner. The speaker crackles as the server asks for your order. You lean out the window of your car and say, "I'll have a beefalo burger, an order of fries, and a chocolate yakow milk shake, please." It could happen. ❖❖

Sample Fact and Opinion Questions

Directions: Circle the correct answer for each question.

1. Which of the following statements is a fact?
   A. ". . . some zonkeys have black and white stripes like a zebra, but only on part of their bodies."
   B. "Their meat is also tastier than buffalo and maybe even better than beef."
   C. "In some ways they may be even better than either their mother or their father."
   D. "It sounds like a joke . . ."

2. Which of the following statements is an opinion?
   A. "Mules have been around for thousands of years."
   B. ". . . new scientific methods have made it possible for ligers and tiglons to be born."
   C. "Although these zonkeys and other hybrids seem unusual today, one day they may all be as common as mules."
   D. "In the wild, you'd never find a lion and a tiger sharing a home and family."

© 1997 Profiles Corporation. DO NOT DUPLICATE.

3. Which of the following statements is an opinion?
   A. "Different kinds of animals do not naturally reproduce together."
   B. "With most hybrids, it's pretty easy to tell which two animals are the parents just by looking at their offspring."
   C. "And, like their hardy buffalo parents, their powerful legs and strong hooves can break through snow to find food to eat."
   D. "Beefaloes don't need to eat corn and other expensive grains like beef cattle do."

Additional Practice Questions

Directions: Circle the correct answer for each question.

4. Why did the author *most likely* write this passage?
   A. to entertain readers with interesting stories
   B. to teach readers about a science topic
   C. to persuade readers to help raise hybrid animals
   D. to inform readers about dangerous animals

5. What is one idea you can get from the passage?
   A. Many types of hybrids can be found in nature.
   B. Someday all animals will be hybrids.
   C. Most hybrid animals do not occur naturally.
   D. Scientists can combine any two animal types.

6. If you wanted to learn more about hybrid animals, which book should you use?
   A. *The Unnatural Zoo*   C. *The World Atlas*
   B. *Animals in the Wild*   D. *Guide to Cattle Ranching*

7. Which sentence *best* tells about this passage?
   A. Scientists have helped make new kinds of animals.
   B. A yakow is a cross between a yak and a cow.
   C. Most hybrid animals work harder than their parents.
   D. Hybrids have the best features of their parents.

8. What is a "hybrid animal"?
   A. an animal that works harder than its parents
   B. an animal that is more good-natured than its parents
   C. an animal that is a cross between two different types of animals
   D. an animal that is much more interesting than other animals

© 1997 Profiles Corporation. DO NOT DUPLICATE.

Lesson 9

Reading Hidden Messages

A writer doesn't always come right out and tell the reader everything directly. Sometimes there are messages hidden within the text. Your job as a reader is to try to find them.

Practice Passage

Directions: Read the passage below. It will be used to help you learn about hidden messages.

1   "Bennnnn-jyyyyyyy," an eerie voice called in the darkness. "Bennnnn-jyyyyyy, where are youuuuuu?" whispered another.

2   Three-year-old Benjy Booth opened his eyes with a start. What was that? Was someone calling his name? Benjy squinted his eyes to peer through the blackness of his bedroom. A large white shape seemed to be floating in his doorway.

3   "Bennnnn-jyyyyyy. I'm coming to get youuuuuu," the shape seemed to say.

4   "Mommy!" Benjy cried. He pulled the covers tightly over his head. He curled up into a tiny ball in the middle of his bed and began to cry loudly.

5   Within seconds his parents were at his side. Mom gently tugged at the blankets to uncover the shaking little boy. Dad reached over and turned on the

© 1997 Profiles Corporation. DO NOT DUPLICATE.

light next to Benjy's bed. It glowed red through the balloon-shaped shade.

6 "It's all right, Honey," Mom said. "Daddy and Mommy are here. Nothing can hurt you."

7 Benjy's chest heaved with each sob. His nose ran. Tears streamed down his cheeks. He wiped his eyes and nose with the sleeve of his Spiderman pajamas.

8 "Tell us what happened, Buddy," Dad said softly.

9 It was hard for Benjy to stop crying. Between sobs he said, "A g-g-ghost! There was a g-ghost in my room. It tried to get me."

10 "Sweetheart, there's no ghost in your room. You see, your room is just like it always was. You must have had a bad dream," Mom said.

11 "What's going on?" a soft voice asked from down the hall. Benjy's big sister Jenny appeared in the doorway, pulling a blue robe over her long white nightgown.

12 "Yeah, what's up?" It was Karen, Jenny's twin, who peeked into the room from behind her. She and Jenny were dressed identically.

13 "Benjy had a bad dream," Mom said. "But he's going to be all right now."

14 Benjy's sobs shook his small body. He peered through wet lashes toward the doorway where moments ago he had seen the ghost. He wasn't quite so scared while Mommy held him. "It wasn't a dream. A g-ghost tried to get me," he said, looking from one girl to the other with tear-filled brown eyes.

15 Jenny and Karen quickly exchanged glances. They didn't have to say a word—as usual, each twin knew what the other was thinking. This was the little bother who got into everything they owned. He was the terror who broke their toys and colored in their books. And he was the same pain-in-the-neck who had gotten them into trouble yesterday when he ratted on them to their father.

16 But now, curled up like a baby on Mom's lap, Benjy suddenly seemed innocent and precious. The ten-year-olds shifted their weight from slippered foot to slippered foot. They kept glancing from Benjy to each other and back again.

17 Mom was too busy cuddling Benjy and cooing comforting words to him to notice what the girls were doing. "It's all right, Honey. Mommy's here," she said.

18 But Dad didn't miss any of it. "Girls, is there something you'd like to tell us?" he asked. He was looking right at them, and he wasn't smiling. ❖❖❖

© 1997 Profiles Corporation. DO NOT DUPLICATE.

Put together details from the passage to find the author's hidden messages.

Hidden messages are like mysteries. If you only have one clue, they're hard to figure out. The more clues you have, the easier it is to solve the mystery. In a reading passage, the clues are the details.

Use details from the story to answer the following question.

1. What do the twins think about their little brother *most* of the time?
   A. He is a bit of a pest.
   B. He is innocent and precious.
   C. He acts like a baby.
   D. He is sweet and cuddly.

In order to answer the question correctly, you have to look for details in the passage.

2. Write down the number of the paragraph that *best* tells what the girls think about Benjy *most* of the time.

   _____

3. Write three details from the paragraph that tell you how the girls feel about their brother *most* of the time.

   a. _____

   _____

   b. _____

   _____

   c. _____

   _____

© 1997 Profiles Corporation. DO NOT DUPLICATE.

Hidden messages require you to draw conclusions based on what you have read.

Sometimes the clues in a passage are so clearly connected that you can't miss them. Other times, you may need to make what's called an "educated guess." When you make an educated guess, you don't have all the information you need. You have to think carefully about whatever you *do* know before you make a decision. An educated guess is not a wild guess, but it's still a guess.

Make an educated guess to answer the next question. Then underline details in the passage that support your answer.

4. What was the ghost that Benjy saw?

_____

_____

 Look for clues that tell you why the author wrote the passage.

Most of the time a writer won't tell the reader directly why he or she wrote a story or article. However, you can figure out the author's purpose if you pay close attention.

First, decide whether the passage is fiction or nonfiction. Fiction passages are most often written **to entertain** the readers. This might include giving the reader a fright or making the reader laugh or cry.

If the writer wants **to frighten the reader**, the story will be scary. If the writer wants **to make the reader laugh**, the story will be funny. If the writer wants **to make the reader cry**, the story will be sad.

Nonfiction passages may be written for several purposes. Sometimes the author wants **to inform** or **to teach** the reader about a topic. These passages are usually filled with facts and little or no opinion. If there are two or more sides to an issue, the writer presents them all as being of equal value.

Sometimes an author wants **to persuade** or **to convince** the reader of a certain viewpoint. These passages are usually filled with **opinions**. If there are two or more sides to an issue, the writer presents one of them as being the best.

© 1997 Profiles Corporation. DO NOT DUPLICATE.

5. What is the author's purpose for writing "The Trouble With Getting Even"?
   A. to entertain the reader with an interesting story
   B. to teach the reader facts about ghosts
   C. to convince the reader that ghosts won't harm them
   D. to persuade the reader not to believe in ghosts

 Look for clues that show you *how* the author is getting his or her message across.

Try to notice the special methods that an author uses to tell the story. This will help you understand the author's message. Here is an example:

6. Why does the author spell the name "Benjy" as "Bennnnn-jyyyyyyy"?
   A. to show how Benjy's name was said in a scary way
   B. to show that the ghost was nervous when it called Benjy
   C. to show that the ghost's voice was very loud
   D. to show how frightened Benjy was when he heard his name

Skim the passage. Try to find where the author used this method in the story. See it in paragraphs 1 and 3? " 'Bennnnn-jyyyyyyy,' an eerie voice called in the darkness. . . ."

Is the voice scary (A), nervous (B), or loud (C)? We know that the voice is eerie, which means that it is creepy and mysterious. An eerie voice can be very scary indeed! So, choice A looks better than choices B or C.

Look at choice D. This could be true if Benjy were calling his own name. But he is not. Someone else is calling, "Bennnnn-jyyyyyyy." So, choice A is still the best choice.

© 1997 Profiles Corporation. DO NOT DUPLICATE.

Sample "Hidden Messages" Questions

Directions: Following are some more questions that ask you to find hidden messages. Circle the correct answer for each question.

1. Why isn't Dad smiling when he looks at the girls at the end of the passage?
   A. He is frightened for Benjy.
   B. He doesn't know what has happened.
   C. He is too tired to smile.
   D. He is angry at the girls.

2. What idea can you get from this passage?
   A. The girls have mixed feelings about their brother.
   B. Mom and Dad love Benjy more than they love the twins.
   C. Benjy is always innocent and precious.
   D. Benjy had a dream about ghosts.

3. What does the fact that the girls "shifted from slippered foot to slippered foot" *most likely* tell us about them?
   A. They were very tired.
   B. They wanted to sit down.
   C. They were feeling guilty.
   D. They were cold.

4. Why does the author spell the word "ghost" as "g-g-ghost"?
   A. to show that Benjy is speaking while he is crying
   B. to show that Benjy doesn't believe it's a real ghost
   C. to show that Benjy is angry at the ghost
   D. to show that Benjy was only dreaming about a ghost

Additional Practice Questions

Directions: Circle the correct answer to each question.

5. An "eerie voice" called Benjy's name. What kind of voice was it?
   A. a very pleasant, cheerful voice
   B. a mysterious, scary voice
   C. a tired-sounding voice
   D. a funny, entertaining voice

6. "Benjy's chest heaved" each time he sobbed. What did Benjy's chest do with each sob?
   A. It stayed very still.
   B. It grew smaller and smaller.
   C. It stopped hurting.
   D. It lifted up suddenly.

© 1997 Profiles Corporation. DO NOT DUPLICATE.

7. What is *most likely* to happen next in the story?
   A. Dad will scare Benjy.
   B. Jenny and Karen will get mad at Benjy.
   C. The twins will tell Dad something.
   D. Another ghost will frighten Benjy.

8. What is the setting of the story?
   A. a boy's bedroom at night
   B. a hallway early in the morning
   C. the twins' bedroom at night
   D. the parents' bedroom in the morning

9. Who is telling this story?
   A. Benjy
   B. Dad
   C. the twins
   D. a narrator who is not part of the story

10. What is the *main* idea of the story?
    A. Two sisters think it is funny to watch their brother cry.
    B. A child is frightened when he thinks he sees a ghost.
    C. A mother and father worry when their little boy is scared by a ghost.
    D. Two sisters comfort their brother when he sees a ghost.

11. What is Benjy's *main* problem in the passage?
    A. He doesn't like his twin sisters.
    B. He is scared by something in his doorway.
    C. He feels bad about waking the family.
    D. He is crying so hard that his nose is running.

12. The twins remember that Benjy had "ratted on them to their father." What did Benjy *most likely* tell their father about?
    A. something kind the twins had done
    B. something silly the twins had said
    C. something bad the twins had done
    D. something fun the twins had taught him

© 1997 Profiles Corporation. DO NOT DUPLICATE.

Lesson 10

What Does *That* Mean?

Whether you're reading for school or for pleasure, you're bound (likely) to encounter (come across) an unfamiliar (strange) word or phrase once in a while. Don't get befuddled (confused). With a few simple strategies (plans of attack), you can decipher (figure out the meaning of) almost any word or phrase you're likely to meet.

 Tip 1 **Look back in the reading passage to find the word or phrase mentioned in the question.**

Some questions will ask you about the meaning of a word or a phrase (group of words). To answer these questions, go back to the reading passage to find where the word or phrase appears.

Once you have found the word or phrase, read the entire sentence surrounding it. You may even need to read the whole paragraph in which it appears. This will help you find the clues you need to understand the meaning of an unfamiliar word or phrase.

Tip 2 **Look for other words in the passage that have about the same meaning.**

If you read carefully, you may find other words in the passage that have the same meaning as the unknown word or phrase.

Read the following passage from *The Summer of the Swans* by Betsy Byars. It tells about a girl named Sara who enjoys watching movies on television.

> She was good, too, at joining in the dialogue with the actors. When the cowboy would say something like, "Things are quiet around here tonight," she would join in with, "Yeah, *too* quiet," right on cue.

1. When a cowboy says something in a show, what does Sara do?

_____

_____

_____

© 1997 Profiles Corporation. DO NOT DUPLICATE.

2. What is the meaning of the word "dialogue"?
   A. action
   B. fun
   C. talk
   D. picture

The passage tells that a cowboy would "say something," and that Sara "would join in." To "say something" and to "join in" by saying words are both talking. You can probably guess that "dialogue" is a conversation—in other words, *talk*.

 Plug the answer choices into the sentence in place of the unknown word or phrase.

Do this to check your answer after you have used tips 1 and 2. Plug the answer choices into the sentence in place of the unknown word or phrase in the passage. The one that makes the most sense in the passage should be the correct answer.

Read the following passage.

> Gilly's heart ached with sorrow. Her best friend Monty was leaving Raleigh to live on a dude ranch in Colorado. Would she ever get over the pain of his leaving?

3. What does "ached" mean?
   A. kept pounding
   B. hurt a lot
   C. thumped loudly
   D. beat slowly

Plug the answer choices into the passage in place of the word "ached." Which choice makes the most sense in the passage? Why do you think so?

_____

_____

_____

_____

EXAMINATION COPY
DO NOT DUPLICATE
©BUCKLE DOWN PUBLISHING CO.

© 1997 Profiles Corporation. DO NOT DUPLICATE.

Practice Passage

Directions: Read the following passage and answer the questions.

Young Night Thoughts

by Robert Louis Stevenson

All night long and every night,
When my mama puts out the light,
I see the people marching by,
As plain as day, before my eye.
Armies and emperors and kings,
All carrying different kinds of things,
And marching in so grand a way,
You never saw the like by day.
So fine a show was never seen
At the great circus on the green;
For every kind of beast and man
Is marching in that caravan.
At first they move a little slow,
But still the faster on they go,
And still beside them close I keep
Until we reach the town of Sleep.

© 1997 Profiles Corporation. DO NOT DUPLICATE.

Sample Vocabulary Questions

Directions: Circle the correct answer for the question.

1. What does the speaker mean by "marching in so grand a way"?
   A. The people are traveling a great distance.
   B. The people are marching in the right direction.
   C. The people look very big and strong.
   D. The people are a wonderful sight to see.

2. What is the meaning of "caravan"?
   A. a large group traveling together
   B. a big party held in one place
   C. a type of circus tent
   D. a type of automobile

3. What happens when the caravan reaches "the town of Sleep"?
   A. The people go back home again.
   B. The speaker is no longer awake.
   C. The armies go to war.
   D. The people set up camp.

Additional Practice Questions

Directions: Circle the correct answer for each question.

4. How often does the speaker see the caravan?
   A. once a year
   B. every summer
   C. every night
   D. once a week

5. How does the speaker feel in the poem?
   A. frightened of the armies
   B. interested in the sight
   C. bored with all the people
   D. worried that he can't march fast

© 1997 Profiles Corporation. DO NOT DUPLICATE.

6. Who is the speaker in the poem?
    A. a child
    B. a mother
    C. a king
    D. a narrator who is not part of the poem

7. Which sentence *best* tells about this poem?
    A. The speaker imagines he is in the army.
    B. The speaker likes circus animals.
    C. The speaker is afraid of the dark at night.
    D. The speaker imagines things before going to sleep.

8. Which lines rhyme in the poem?
    A. Each pair of lines rhymes.
    B. Every other line rhymes.
    C. The first and last lines rhyme.
    D. No lines rhyme.

9. If you wanted to learn more about the life of Robert Louis Stevenson, which book should you use?
    A. *The Children's Poetry Collection*
    B. *The Encyclopedia of Poets and Authors*
    C. *Poems of Emperors and Kings*
    D. *Tips for a Deeper Sleep*

© 1997 Profiles Corporation. DO NOT DUPLICATE.

Unit 4 **Review**

Directions: Read the passage below and answer the questions that follow.

From

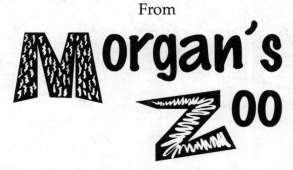

Morgan's Zoo

by James Howe

Morgan is a zookeeper at the Chelsea Park Zoo. Clarence, a chimpanzee, is like a son to Morgan. One morning Morgan is told by his boss that the zoo will be closed and Clarence will be sent away the next day. Allison and Andrew, Morgan's young friends, come up with a plan to save Clarence by pretending that he is Morgan's nephew and hiding him in Morgan's apartment. But can they fool Morgan's nearsighted landlady, Miss Twillery?

When the taxi driver glanced into his rearview mirror, his cigar almost fell out of his mouth.

"Where ya headed, Mac?" he asked Morgan. "The circus?"

Morgan tried to remain calm. He was still not convinced that this little scheme the twins had cooked up was going to work at all. Clarence sat at his side, neatly dressed in a shirt, tie, pants held up by suspenders, an old pair of running shoes, and a large hat Morgan hoped would help disguise his true identity. So far it didn't seem to be working.

"No," he said to the driver. Then, giving his address, he added, "This is my nephew. He's come to visit me."

At that, the driver jerked round in his seat. He stared at Clarence, then at Morgan, and then shook his head. "Well, for your sake," he said at last, "I hope whatever he's got don't run in the family."

Morgan breathed deeply as the taxi pulled away from the curb to carry him and his "nephew" home. It had been a long day, and he would be glad when it was over. One hope he nurtured: that Miss Twillery would not be sitting out front on the porch, as was her custom on summer afternoons. Perhaps, because he had waited till the dinner hour, she would be in her kitchen, and he would escape her notice.

© 1997 Profiles Corporation. DO NOT DUPLICATE.

But as the taxi pulled up before the house, he saw at once that such good fortune was not to be his. There she sat as always, doggedly rocking and just as doggedly fanning away the summer heat. Nervously, Morgan paid the driver and opened the door of the taxi.

"Now, Clarence," he whispered as he took his charge's hand, "try to behave as much like a little boy as you know how. Just think about Andrew and do what he would do." In his other hand, Morgan carried the valise that Allison had been smart enough to think of.

"After all," she'd told Morgan and Andrew, "we can't have Morgan arrive with his nephew and no suitcase. What would Miss Twillery say?"

What Miss Twillery *did* say was, "Good evening, Morgan. My, aren't you working late today?"

"Evening, Miss Twillery," replied Morgan casually, as if arriving home with a chimpanzee on his arm was something he did every night. "I'm late," he went on, "because I had to pick up my nephew at the train station. He's come in from Cincinnati to pay me a visit."

"Well, isn't that nice?" said Miss Twillery. She stopped rocking then and leaned forward, squinting fiercely. The bun of blonde hair that she wore atop her head (which Morgan suspected wasn't nature's gift) toppled forward slightly. She gave it a shove with her hand as she smiled at the figure standing next to Morgan.

"Hello, young man," she said in a syrupy voice. "And what is *your* name?" Miss Twillery had a way of speaking to children that, were Clarence really a child, would have made him want to kick her.

"His name is Tommy," Morgan said quickly.

"Tommy," cooed Miss Twillery. "Isn't that a *nice* name? And how old are you, Tommy, dear?"

"He's seven," replied Morgan.

Miss Twillery extended her hand. "How do you do, Tommy?" she said.

© 1997 Profiles Corporation. DO NOT DUPLICATE.

Clarence understood the meaning of her gesture and reached out to place his hand in hers accordingly.

Miss Twillery gasped. "Oh, my! What a large hand for such a small child."

Feeling beads of sweat form on his brow, Morgan stammered, "It's . . . that is . . . he's . . . he's wearing a baseball mitt."

"Ah," said Miss Twillery, releasing Clarence's hand. "Well, I suppose boys will be boys. Still, he's an awfully quiet one, isn't he?"

"He's shy," Morgan said. In an effort to look the part, Clarence hung his head and dragged his sneakered toe back and forth across the floor.

"Well, *I* was shy when I was his age," Miss Twillery said simperingly. "I certainly know how he feels." She leaned toward Clarence and looked deeply into his eyes. "Tommy, you and I shall have to spend some time together," she said. "Then you won't feel so shy."

Morgan was frantically trying to think of a response when Miss Twillery turned to face him. "Why, Morgan," she said. "I've just noticed something about Tommy I hadn't seen before."

"What's that?" Morgan asked nervously. He was sure the game was up.

"He looks just like you. How silly of me not to have seen the family resemblance at once." ❖❖

© 1997 Profiles Corporation. DO NOT DUPLICATE.

Unit 4 Review Questions

Directions: Circle the correct answer for each question.

1. Why does the taxi driver almost drop his cigar?
   A. He can't talk with a cigar in his mouth.
   B. He knows he shouldn't smoke in his taxi cab.
   C. He is startled by something he sees.
   D. He is afraid of the chimpanzee.

2. Why does the driver say to Morgan, "Well, for your sake, I hope whatever he's got don't run in the family"?
   A. He thinks Clarence is strange-looking for a boy.
   B. He believes Clarence has an illness that Morgan might catch.
   C. He wants to wish Morgan happiness with his new family.
   D. He thinks that Clarence has stolen something.

3. Who had the idea to dress Clarence up as Morgan's nephew?
   A. Clarence
   B. the twins
   C. Morgan
   D. Miss Twillery

4. What is the purpose of the paragraph that comes before the passage?
   A. It summarizes what has happened earlier in the story.
   B. It tells why the author is writing the story.
   C. It explains a lesson that will be learned in the story.
   D. It gives the reader hints about how the story will end.

5. What is the "valise" that Morgan is carrying?
   A. a shirt
   B. a suitcase
   C. a walking stick
   D. a hat

© 1997 Profiles Corporation. DO NOT DUPLICATE.

6. Which of the following is a statement of fact?
    A. "This is my nephew."
    B. "... he's an awfully quiet one, isn't he?"
    C. "What a large hand for such a small child."
    D. "So far it didn't seem to be working."

7. What does the author mean when he states that Morgan suspects that Miss Twillery's bun "wasn't nature's gift"?
    A. Her hair is too long to wear in a bun.
    B. Her bun does not look like her real hair.
    C. Her hairstyle is not very attractive.
    D. Her bun is much too large for her head.

8. What is the *main* purpose of the passage?
    A. to teach the reader
    B. to entertain the reader
    C. to persuade the reader
    D. to frighten the reader

EXAMINATION COPY
DO NOT DUPLICATE
©BUCKLE DOWN PUBLISHING CO.

Additional Practice Questions

Directions: Now try answering some other types of questions about the reading passage. Circle the correct answer for each question.

9. What is the setting of the story?
    A. a city in the summer
    B. a zoo in the spring
    C. a circus in the summer
    D. a farm in autumn

10. What is Morgan's *main* problem?
    A. Miss Twillery is on her front porch.
    B. He is trying to hide a chimpanzee.
    C. He has to ride home in a taxi cab.
    D. He doesn't have the right clothes for Clarence.

11. How is the driver's reaction to Clarence different from Miss Twillery's reaction?

    A. He accepts Clarence as Morgan's nephew.

    B. He shakes Clarence's hand in a friendly way.

    C. He doesn't seem to believe Morgan's story about Clarence.

    D. He thinks Clarence has a very large hand.

12. Who is telling this story?

    A. Morgan

    B. Clarence

    C. the twins

    D. a narrator who is not part of the story

13. Which of the following choices *best* completes the character map?

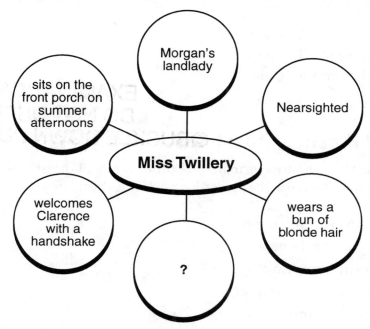

    A. thinks Clarence belongs in the circus

    B. is in her kitchen when Morgan and Clarence arrive

    C. thinks Clarence has a small hand

    D. notices how much Clarence looks like Morgan

© 1997 Profiles Corporation. DO NOT DUPLICATE.

Going Beyond the Passage

UNIT 5

Applying What You Read

Some of the questions on the reading test will ask you to connect information from the passage to a new situation. Read the following passage to learn more about application questions.

Practice Passage

The following information is from a travel brochure. It tells about some of the interesting features of North Carolina.

From tall mountain ranges to sandy white beaches, you'll love the variety North Carolina has to offer. Interesting history, breathtaking scenery, and endless opportunities for fun and entertainment are just a few of the things we have in store.

Mountain Region

Our pleasant climate, beautiful flowers, and colorful fall leaves bring visitors from all over the world to our Blue Ridge and Great Smoky Mountains.

If you like adventure, climb Mount Mitchell near Asheville, the highest peak east of the Mississippi River. Explore the Brevard area, the Land of Waterfalls. Marvel at the many waterfalls in the area, including Whitewater Falls, the highest waterfall in the Eastern United States. Be sure to go fishing on the New River, but don't let its name fool you. New River is the second-oldest river in the world.

© 1997 Profiles Corporation. DO NOT DUPLICATE.

National Forests, state parks, and many private resorts offer hiking, camping, boating, swimming, skiing, and other outdoor activities. The Cherokee Indian Reservation is a great place to learn about Native American history and culture. And if grand houses are what you want to see, don't miss the 255-room Biltmore Estate near Asheville.

Central Region

Of course, North Carolina is chock full of history. Many historic villages and landmarks in the Central Region recall our country's past. Famous battles of the Revolutionary and Civil War will come to life as you roam our many battlefields.

Be sure to make a stop at the North Carolina Zoological Park near Asheboro, the world's largest natural habitat zoo. When the sun goes down, enjoy world-class entertainment. Music, theater, and the arts thrive in our fair cities. And, of course, don't forget to join us for nationally ranked college basketball.

Coastal Region

Rest your heels on one of our many beaches. Climb a lighthouse and look out over the waves of the Atlantic Ocean. Imagine yourself watching Orville and Wilbur Wright making their first airplane flight when you visit the Wright Brothers National Memorial near Kitty Hawk.

Visit Roanoke Island, the location of the first English settlement in America. And be sure not to miss Ocracoke Island, once the hideout of the famous pirate, Blackbeard.

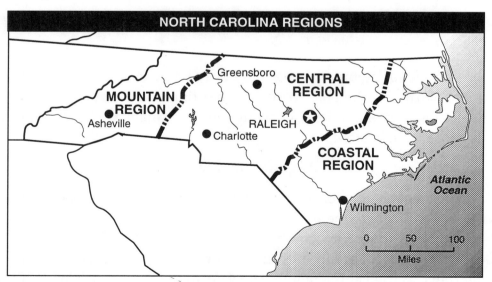

Whether it's history, scenery, or entertainment, North Carolina has what you're looking for. But even with all this, we think that the best thing about our state is its people. Come sample our friendliness. You'll be welcomed in true Southern style.

© 1997 Profiles Corporation. DO NOT DUPLICATE.

Read the question carefully.

The question will give you clues to where you can find the correct answer in the passage.

Read the question below.

1. If a family wants to vacation near waterfalls, where would be the *best* place for them to visit?

Circle a key word in the question above that might help you find the correct answer in the passage.

 Skim the passage for key words from the question.

Once you have found the key word or words in the question, skim the passage. Can you find the word *waterfalls* in the passage?

Read the sentences in the passage that the contain the word *waterfalls*. Then read the question below and choose the best answer.

1. If a family wants to vacation near waterfalls, where would be the *best* place for them to visit?
    A. the area near Brevard in the Mountain Region
    B. the Biltmore Estate near Asheville
    C. the Cherokee Indian Reservation
    D. Roanoke Island off the coast

© 1997 Profiles Corporation. DO NOT DUPLICATE.

Tip 3 **Try to put yourself in the situation.**

Imagine that you are in the situation described by the question. Thinking about what *you* would do in the situation will help you decide on an answer. But remember, you must still use information in the passage to help you choose your answer.

Read the question below.

2. What might be the *best* reason to recommend this passage to a friend?
   A. It would tell her which college basketball games to see.
   B. It would help her write a history report.
   C. It would teach her how to camp in the outdoors.
   D. It would help her plan a trip in North Carolina.

Imagine someone just recommended the passage to *you* to read. How would the passage help *you* most?

Look at choice A. The passage mentions that some of the basketball teams in North Carolina are very good. But would this passage tell you which college basketball games to watch? No. Cross out choice A.

Look at choice B. The passage mentions that there are many historical sites in North Carolina. But does it tell you enough details about history to write a history report? No. Cross out choice B.

Look at choice C. The passage mentions that there are several places to go camping in North Carolina. But does it teach you any camping skills? No. Cross out choice C.

Look at choice D. The passage tells about many things you could see and do in North Carolina. It also tells you a little about what the different regions of the state are like. You may need more information to plan a trip, but this passage could get you started. Choice D is the correct answer.

© 1997 Profiles Corporation. DO NOT DUPLICATE.

Use information from the passage to make your choice.

Application questions ask you to use information from the passage in a new situation. But you still have to base your answers on information in the passage. Take the following question, for example.

3. Students in Ms. Jackson's class were asked to tell the *main* reason people like to visit North Carolina's mountains in October.

    Jeni said, "The warm sunshine brings many people to the beaches."

    Jay said, "There are interesting animals at the zoo in Asheboro."

    Doria said, "The leaves on the trees turn many beautiful colors."

    Dan said, "The heavy snows make winter a great time for skiing."

    Which student answered correctly?
    A. Jeni
    B. Jay
    C. Doria
    D. Dan

Start by circling key words in the first part of the question. One key word that will give you a clue is *mountains*. You should go back to the paragraphs under the heading titled "Mountain Region." Read those paragraphs again.

Another key word in the question is *October*. Is the word *October* mentioned in the paragraphs you just read? No, but the first sentence in the "Mountain Region" section mentions that people visit there to see the "colorful fall leaves." October is in the fall.

Now read the choices again. Which choice looks best? _____

© 1997 Profiles Corporation. DO NOT DUPLICATE.

100

Sample Application Questions

Directions: Circle the correct answer for each question.

1. Which of the following sites would a visitor probably have the *least* luck finding in North Carolina?
   A. a village restored to look like it did in the 1700s
   B. a statue honoring soldiers killed in a Civil War battle
   C. a theater where you can see great plays performed
   D. a museum about how cowboys lived in the Wild West

2. On a trip to the Central Region, you would have the *most* luck finding which of the following?
   A. a lighthouse
   B. a very tall mountain
   C. a natural habitat zoo
   D. a pirate's hideout

3. On a trip to the coastal region of North Carolina, you would be *most likely* to find which of the following?
   A. the second oldest river
   B. the first English settlement
   C. the tallest mountain peak
   D. a 255-room house

4. If you want to see where the first airplane flight was taken, which area of the state should you visit?
   A. the mountains
   B. the central part of the state
   C. the area near the coast
   D. the waterfalls

© 1997 Profiles Corporation. DO NOT DUPLICATE.

Additional Practice Questions

Directions: Circle the correct answers for each question.

5. What could the author have added to make the article *most* useful to someone planning a vacation in North Carolina?
   A. a list of phone numbers to call for more information on the places mentioned
   B. pictures of some of the cities in the central region
   C. a chart showing the win-loss records of college basketball teams in the state
   D. a map of all the rooms in Biltmore Estate near Asheville

6. How does the map help you understand the article?
   A. It shows how to get to North Carolina from other states.
   B. It shows what the different regions of the state look like.
   C. It shows where the regions mentioned in the article are located.
   D. It shows exactly where the most interesting places are located.

7. What would be the *best* way to find out more about things to do and see in North Carolina?
   A. ask someone who lives in Charlotte
   B. read a book about the Wright Brothers
   C. watch a movie about the pirate Bluebeard
   D. ask your local librarian for more information

8. What is the author's purpose in writing this passage?
   A. to tell an entertaining story
   B. to argue against an idea
   C. to persuade people to do something
   D. to explain how something works

9. What did the author provide to help you better understand the passage?
   A. numbers telling how many people visit North Carolina each year
   B. dates of important events that happened in North Carolina's history
   C. headings to help you sort information about the different regions of the state
   D. statements from people who live in North Carolina telling why others should visit the state

© 1997 Profiles Corporation. DO NOT DUPLICATE.

Using Resources

Imagine that you've just read about an interesting topic, like a do-it-yourself rocket ship or a ten-year-old who became a millionaire. You'd like to learn more about the subject, but where do you go for more information?

Most often, the first place to look is the reference section of your school library. There you can find atlases, encyclopedias, dictionaries, almanacs, and many other helpful books. Once you learn how to use these reference sources, you'll be able to find information on nearly every topic.

One kind of question on the North Carolina test will ask you to judge different types of resources. These questions are trying to find out whether you know how to use resources to help you learn. This lesson will help you answer those questions *and* improve your skills in using resources.

 Tip 1 **Read the question carefully.**

Resource questions might be asked in several different ways on the test. Here are some examples:

> What would be the *best* way to find out more about the topic of the passage?

> What would be the *best* way to make sure the information in this passage is correct?

> What would help you *most* to understand this passage?

Read the question carefully. Think about the topic or main idea of the passage. It will be an important clue to finding the correct answer.

Tip 2 **Decide what general subject area the topic fits into.**

When you look up a topic in a reference book, you may not find it listed by name. For example, imagine that you want to learn about the feeding habits of a housefly. You could start by going to the index of an encyclopedia and looking for "feeding habits." That probably wouldn't get you very far. So then you might try looking up "housefly."

© 1997 Profiles Corporation. DO NOT DUPLICATE.

You find "housefly" listed in the index, but it tells you, *"See Insects."* That makes sense, because a housefly is an insect. Next, you look in the index under "Insects." Aha! Here's the word "housefly" with a page number next to it. Now you can find out what you really want to know: how much does a housefly eat in a day?

Look at the list of topics below. Draw a line to match each topic with the category it most likely belongs with.

1. Bill Clinton	A. recording artists
2. a broken kitchen faucet	B. royalty
3. *The Lion King*	C. health
4. singer Janet Jackson	D. Presidents
5. Queen Elizabeth II	E. plumbing
6. model airplanes	F. movies
7. exercise guidelines	G. hobbies

Tip 3   **Know what kinds of information are in the different types of reference books.**

An **almanac** is published every year. It contains **facts** about all kinds of topics. This information is very up-to-date. The facts change each year.

Use an almanac to find lists of facts, such as:

- population of major cities
- major products of each state
- important events that took place during the year
- names of famous people
- movies that won awards that year

An **atlas** is a book filled with **maps**. There are many different kinds of atlases. Some atlases show maps of a certain part of the world, like the *Atlas of the United States.* Others, like *The World Atlas,* have maps of the entire world.

The land features shown in atlases don't change from year to year. However, the borders of nations may change as governments take over new territory or give up control of an area. Names of cities sometimes change, too.

© 1997 Profiles Corporation. DO NOT DUPLICATE.

Use an atlas to find the location of:

- borders and boundaries (between counties, states, nations, etc.)
- bodies of water (oceans, glaciers, rivers, lakes, etc.)
- land formations (continents, mountain ranges, deserts, plains, etc.)
- population facts (cities, countries, etc.)

A **dictionary** is a book filled with the **words** that make up a language. It doesn't change much from year to year, although a few new words are added from time to time. An American English dictionary contains the English words that are spoken in the United States. All the words are listed in alphabetical order from A to Z.

Use a dictionary to find out:
- correct spellings
- definitions
- parts of speech (like "verb," "noun," or "adjective")

An **encyclopedia** contains facts and explanations about a wide variety of subjects. The topics are arranged in alphabetical order. Some encyclopedias, like the *World Book Encyclopedia*, contain information about almost every subject you could think of. Others, like the *Encyclopedia of Winter Sports* or the *Encyclopedia of American Artists*, only discuss certain kinds of topics.

Use an encyclopedia when you need more information than a dictionary or atlas can give you.

 Think about other ways to find information on the topic.

There are all kinds of ways to learn about a topic. A few possible resources are described below.

A **biography** is a book about someone's life. If you want to learn more about Amelia Earhart, the first female airplane pilot to cross the Atlantic alone, you can read a biography of her life.

Newspapers are usually printed daily. They have articles about important day-to-day events. If you want to learn about what the President said yesterday in a speech, you would probably look in a newspaper.

Magazines contain articles about all kinds of things. Some magazines have articles about different types of hobbies—listening to music, drawing and painting, cooking, or building and repairing things. Other magazines, like *Sports Illustrated for Kids*, have articles about sports. Magazines can even have stories in them, like the ones in *American Girl* and *Boys' Life*.

© 1997 Profiles Corporation. DO NOT DUPLICATE.

Magazines like *Newsweek* and *Time* contain information about important events in the news. But magazines come out less often than newspapers do. They usually have less information about day-to-day events than newspapers.

A **brochure** is a very short booklet that tells about only one topic. A brochure is often used to describe things. If you were planning a trip to Raleigh, you might call the Capital Area Visitor Center and ask them to send you a brochure showing all the interesting places to visit there.

People can be excellent resources. If you want to find out what kinds of trees and other wildlife are in the Pisgah National Forest, you can call a forest ranger who works there. You might be surprised to find out how much you can learn just by asking.

 Decide what type of resource each answer choice represents.

The answer choices will often give you clues about what type of reference materials they are. Look at the list of titles below. On the line next to each title, write one of the following:

- almanac
- atlas
- dictionary
- biography
- newspaper
- magazine
- encyclopedia
- brochure
- other (any other type of resource)

EXAMINATION COPY DO NOT DUPLICATE ©BUCKLE DOWN PUBLISHING CO.

8. *Maps of the Western Hemisphere* _____

9. *Words and Phrases from the South* _____

10. *Raising Worms for Fun and Profit* _____

11. *The Model Railroad Encyclopedia* _____

12. *The 1996 Book of Facts* _____

13. *Heroic Women of the Civil War* _____

14. *Reader's Digest* _____

15. *Elizabeth Dole: A Life of Public Service* _____

16. *The Charlotte Observer* _____

17. *National Geographic World* _____

© 1997 Profiles Corporation. DO NOT DUPLICATE.

Look for other clues in the question or answer choices.

Sometimes the answer choices will all seem very much alike. You will have to decide which one is most correct. Let's take a look at a sample question and its possible answers.

First, imagine that you just read a passage about the Big Dipper and Little Dipper constellations. It told a story that ancient people had made up to explain the presence of these constellations in the sky. Pretend that the question below followed the passage.

18. Which of the following would be a good book to use to find out more about constellation stories?
    A. *Legends of the Night Sky*
    B. *Slaves Follow the North Star to Freedom*
    C. *"Star Light, Star Bright" and Other Children's Poems*
    D. *Star Gazer's Guide: A Map of the Constellations*

The questions below ask you about how you answered question number 18.

• First think about the question. What are "constellation stories"?

_____

_____

Now look at the answer choices. They all have something to do with stars or the sky.

• Look at answer choice A. What does the word "Legends" suggest about the book?

_____

• Look carefully at answer choice B. What do you think it is mostly about?

_____

_____

• Look at answer choice C. What words tell you what this book is mostly about?

_____

_____

© 1997 Profiles Corporation. DO NOT DUPLICATE.

- Look at answer choice D. What do you think it is mostly about?

  _____

- What is the correct answer to question 18?

  _____

 Tip 7   **Look for resources given along with the passage.**

Sometimes the author will give you charts, pictures, maps, or other things to help you understand the passage. A few examples are described below.

A passage about the different kinds of people that make up our country might include a **list** of common American words that come from other countries. A passage about the Amazon River might give you a **map** of the river.

If a passage is about a terrific new invention that turns tap water into a fizzy cola, the author might give a **picture** or **illustration** that shows how the invention works.

The passage may contain several different topics under the main topic. In this case, the author might put a **subheading** in bold type above each subtopic. Subheadings help you keep the different ideas in the passage straight in your mind.

Sometimes a passage may contain **footnotes** that explain ideas in the passage. Small raised numbers (like this[1]) refer you to notes at the bottom of the page.

Tip 8   **Look for the answer choice that will give you the MOST information about the topic.**

The question below might follow a passage about how to set up your own tropical fish tank. Find the choices that would give you the most information about this topic.

19. What would be the best way to check to see if the information in this passage is accurate?
    A. watch a movie about deep sea divers
    B. read a book about keeping tropical fish as pets
    C. ask a neighbor who goes fishing often
    D. look up the word *fish* in a dictionary

All of the choices would probably tell you something about fish. But which choice would tell you the *most* about setting up a tropical fish tank?

© 1997 Profiles Corporation. DO NOT DUPLICATE.

Practice Passage

Directions: Read the passage below and answer the questions that follow.

TARANTULA!

by Karen Nichols

Have you ever been frightened by a spider? Sometimes even the little ones look a bit creepy crawling around. But what about BIG, HAIRY spiders? Now those can be really scary!

The old saying, "Don't judge a book by its cover" can be applied to spiders, too. Even the most frightening-looking ones—tarantulas—aren't as harmful as you might think. In spite of what you may have seen on TV or in the movies, people rarely die from a tarantula bite.

There are many different kinds of tarantulas. The bird spider, a type of tarantula found in South America, is very large. Its body can be as long as $3\frac{1}{2}$ inches. When it spreads its legs, it is large enough to cover a dinner plate! It is called a bird spider because it lives in trees and eats small birds. Other tarantulas—such as the ones that live in Brazil—eat small reptiles and amphibians.

The tarantula's poisonous bite helps it kill insects and other small animals for food. The bite of some kinds of tarantulas can be very serious for humans. Most of these dangerous spiders—like the funnel-web spider of Australia— live in other parts of the world. Tarantulas that live in the United States are far less harmful to humans. To be bitten by one of these wouldn't be pleasant, but for the most part it would be about as serious as being stung by a bee.

One tarantula found in the United States is called the trap-door spider. It grows to be about an inch long. For its home, it digs a burrow in the ground and covers it with a hinged door made of mud and its own silk. It also lines the burrow with silk to make a comfortable nest for its young.

The trap-door spider is shy; most females hardly ever leave their nests. They don't really have to. The trap-door spider simply waits just inside its burrow for some unsuspecting prey to walk by. When it senses the footsteps of its victim, it throws open the door, grabs the animal, and poisons it. Then the tarantula drags its victim inside.

Tarantulas are in danger of being eaten themselves. Birds, mice, and other tarantulas try to kill them for food. But tarantulas have many defenses. Sometimes they try to scare away their enemies. They stand up on their hind legs and flash their big fangs. They may also rub their jaws together to make a loud *H-I-S-S* sound.

© 1997 Profiles Corporation. DO NOT DUPLICATE.

Other tarantulas have an even more interesting way to scare off animals that might be looking for a furry meal. These tarantulas are covered with thousands of tiny hairs. When they rub their legs together, the hairs fly off their bodies and into the eyes, nose, and mouth of their attacker. The hairs have tiny hooks on them, so you can imagine how this trick might send an enemy packing!

Even with these great defenses, many tarantulas are eaten by other animals while they are still young. But some tarantulas live very long lives, even up to 20 years—or longer. ❖❖

Sample Resources Questions

Directions: Circle the correct answer for the question.

1. If you wanted to find out how to pronounce the word "tarantula," what book should you look in?

   A. a dictionary
   B. an atlas
   C. an almanac
   D. an encyclopedia

2. If you wanted to learn as much as you could about the South American bird spider, in which book should you look?

   A. an atlas
   B. a dictionary
   C. an almanac
   D. an encyclopedia

3. If you wanted to find out more about trap-door spiders, which book should you look in?

   A. *Atlas of the Western States*
   B. *Spiders That Kill Humans*
   C. *Tarantulas Found in the United States*
   D. *The Tarantula's Enemies*

4. If you wanted to learn about ways animals escape becoming someone else's dinner, in which book should you look?

   A. *The Picture Dictionary of Spiders and Other Creepy Crawlers*
   B. *You Can't Eat Me! How Animals Defend Themselves*
   C. *The Animal Lover's Guide to Meatless Meals*
   D. *How to Collect Spiders*

5. What would be the *best* way to check to see if the information in this passage is correct?

   A. look up the word *tarantula* in an encyclopedia
   B. ask someone who owns a pet spider
   C. look up the word *tarantula* in a dictionary
   D. carefully reread the passage

© 1997 Profiles Corporation. DO NOT DUPLICATE.

6. The information in this passage would be *least* useful in writing a report about what?
   A. poisonous spiders of the Americas
   B. defenses used by spiders against their enemies
   C. techniques used by spiders to get food
   D. famous movies about killer spiders

7. What could the author have added to help you better understand this passage?
   A. a chart showing the types of tarantulas, their features, and the countries they live in
   B. a picture of a person being frightened by a South American bird spider
   C. numbers telling how many people are bitten by tarantulas each year
   D. a list showing the word for *spider* in several languages

8. In which source would you *most likely* find the information in this passage?
   A. in a magazine about science
   B. in an article in a daily newspaper
   C. in a travel brochure about South America
   D. in a biography of a famous scientist

9. How does the illustration help you understand the passage?
   A. It shows how large a bird spider is.
   B. It shows where the funnel-web spider lives.
   C. It shows how the trap-door spider waits inside its burrow.
   D. It shows how the Brazilian spider eats small animals.

10. If you did *not* understand this passage, each of the following would help you better understand it *except* which one?
    A. look up additional information about tarantulas
    B. look up the definitions to words you don't know
    C. read an article about how to treat an insect bite
    D. use clues in the passage to figure out unfamiliar words

11. What would be the *best* way to find out whether a tarantula would make a good pet?
    A. ask someone who owns many pets
    B. talk to someone who works at a pet store
    C. read an article on how to take care of a pet
    D. go to the zoo and observe a tarantula's habits

© 1997 Profiles Corporation. DO NOT DUPLICATE.

Additional Practice Questions

Directions: Now try answering some other types of questions about the reading passage. Circle the correct answer for each question.

12. Why does a tarantula make a loud *H-I-S-S* sound?
    A. to find out if an insect is nearby
    B. to scare off an attacker
    C. to attract small birds for food
    D. to attract other spiders

13. What does the writer mean by saying that a tarantula shooting its hairs "might send an enemy packing"?
    A. It will send the enemy away.
    B. It will be able to capture its enemy.
    C. It will hurt its enemy.
    D. It will pull its enemy into its nest.

14. Which of the following is a statement of opinion?
    A. "Sometimes even the little ones look a bit creepy crawling around."
    B. "The tarantula's poisonous bite helps it kill insects and other small animals for food."
    C. "When they rub their legs together, the hairs fly off their bodies and into the eyes, nose, and mouth of their attacker."
    D. "Birds, mice, and other tarantulas try to kill them for food."

15. How do you think the author wants you to feel about tarantulas?
    A. She wants you to be afraid of them.
    B. She wants you to be angry at them.
    C. She wants you to think they are funny.
    D. She wants you to think they are interesting.

© 1997 Profiles Corporation. DO NOT DUPLICATE.

Unit 5 **Review**

Directions: Read the passage below and answer the questions that follow.

From

by J.M. Wasson

Willy entered Dr. Wolfe's waiting room slowly. With superhuman effort he forced one foot in front of the other.

"I'm like a condemned man walking to the electric chair," he thought.

Willy was afraid of dentists, though he really didn't know why. He hadn't even been to a dentist since he was four, and he was nine now. To be fair, Doc Trimble, Willy's last dentist, hadn't been too crazy about seeing Willy either—not after he had almost lost the tips of three fingers in Willy's mouth.

But Doc Trimble had retired six months ago, and now Dr. Wolfe was taking over. At this news, Willy's mother had decided it was high time her son had a checkup.

When Willy had told his best friend Zoey that he couldn't play soccer on Saturday because he was stuck with a dentist appointment, she'd grabbed his arm. "Don't go, Willy! Dr. Wolfe and her assistant are really creepy. Tyrone said his Uncle Mike went last Wednesday, and he hasn't been the same since. Every time anyone talks to him he curls up into a little ball and whimpers like a scared dog."

"Yea, sure, Zoey," Willy had replied. "You know I'm scared of dentists and you're just trying to get back at me for telling my brother you have a crush on him."

But Zoey had kept insisting. Willy had meant to ask Tyrone about his Uncle Mike, but Tyrone hadn't been in school for the last couple of days. So Willy had forgotten about the conversation. Until now.

© 1997 Profiles Corporation. DO NOT DUPLICATE.

"This place sure smells strange," Willy thought. He couldn't quite place the odor. It reminded him of his dog Fritz. No, that wasn't quite it, either. The zoo! That was it. The smell reminded him of the wolf pen at the zoo! Maybe Zoey was telling the truth, after all. He turned and lunged at the door, but his mother's large frame blocked his escape.

"No you don't, Willy," she said. "You're not leaving here until Dr. Wolfe is finished with you."

Willy took a seat in one of the waiting room's blood-red chairs. His imagination gave him no peace. What if the dentist hurt him—really hurt him? Would he bleed all over the place? Or, if he had to have a cavity filled, would she give him a shot—with a needle—a foot-long NEEDLE!? Would he blubber like some baby? Worse yet, what if she pulled out all of his teeth? He'd die of embarrassment gumming his lunch in front of all the other guys at school.

"Willy Carter?" a woman said from the doorway of the inner office. She was dressed in a white nurse's uniform. A lab coat hung loosely from her thin body.

She said it again, with authority this time, "Willy Carter."

Willy didn't answer. Maybe if he ignored her, she'd give up and go on to the next patient. Only there weren't any other patients today.

"Speak up, son," Mrs. Carter said. "There's nothing to be afraid of. Dr. Wolfe won't bite."

"Yes, Ma'am," Willy managed to squeak. "Nothing to be afraid of."

"I'm Dr. Wolfe's assistant, Miss Lupine." Her eyes narrowed into slits as Willy stepped forward. She seemed to be sizing him up, like a dog eyeing a bone and wondering if it would be worth the trouble of burying.

Burying! Oh no, why couldn't he just relax and keep his mind focused on more pleasant things? Like riding his bike around the neighborhood when he got home. Or learning how to do Cat's Cradle with his yo-yo. Willy smiled at the thought of impressing his friends with his great skill at yo-yoing. One of these days he'd be River City's yo-yo champion for sure . . .

"Willy," his mother interrupted his daydreaming. "I'm going to the grocery store while you're in with the dentist. You can take the bus home when you're through." Mrs. Carter pulled open the heavy oak door and stepped into the sunlight outside. She turned to face him. "Willy," she added, "I'm trusting you to behave yourself." She stared at him until his knees shook, then closed the door firmly behind her.

"Come along, Willy," the woman said sternly. "Let's not keep the dentist waiting. It's almost time for her lunch."

Dr. Wolfe's assistant led Willy into an examining room. It didn't look anything like he remembered from his long-ago visit to Doc Trimble. There was no reclining patient's chair, no overhead light to blind the patient, no drill or other tools of dental torture. The room was completely empty. And there were bars on the windows—to keep burglars from breaking in, he supposed. "This place is weird," Willy thought. He shivered nervously.

"The doctor will eat—uh, treat—you in a minute," the assistant said.

© 1997 Profiles Corporation. DO NOT DUPLICATE.

EXAMINATION COPY DO NOT DUPLICATE ©BUCKLE DOWN PUBLISHING CO.

Willy looked up at her in panic.

"Just a little joke to soften up our tough customers," she said with an odd smile. Was he imagining, or had she just run her tongue over her upper lip?

"Some joke," Willy mumbled through clenched teeth.

As the door closed behind the bony woman, Willy heard a soft click. "Hey, Lady, wait a minute," he said. He pulled on the door handle—hard—but it was locked! He was trapped—trapped in the one place he feared more than any in the world. "Someone let me out of here!" he cried. The only reply was a harsh barking laugh from the next room. ❖❖

© 1997 Profiles Corporation. DO NOT DUPLICATE.

Unit 5 Review Questions

Directions: Circle the correct answer for each question.

1. What might be the *best* reason for recommending this passage to a friend?
   A. It tells an entertaining story.
   B. It would help someone who is afraid of dentists.
   C. It would make someone afraid of dentists.
   D. It gives tips on how to avoid werewolves.

2. If Willy suspected that the dentist and her assistant were not human, which book would be the *best* source to help him find out?
   A. *The Encyclopedia of Monsters*
   B. *No More Nightmares: A Guide to Restful Sleep*
   C. *Relax! It's Only a Toothache*
   D. *Choosing Your Dentist*

Additional Practice Questions

Directions: Circle the correct answer for each question.

3. Who is telling the story?
   A. Willy Carter
   B. Dr. Wolfe
   C. Willie's mother
   D. a narrator who is not part of the story

4. What does Willy mean when he says he's "like a condemned man walking to the electric chair"?
   A. He is going someplace he really doesn't want to go.
   B. He is in terrible trouble for doing something wrong.
   C. He is in jail waiting to be sentenced for a crime.
   D. He is trying to sneak out of the dentist's office.

5. Why hadn't Doc Trimble wanted to see Willy?
   A. Willy didn't have any cavities.
   B. Willy had bitten Doc Trimble's fingertips.
   C. Willy was Dr. Wolfe's patient.
   D. Doc Trimble didn't want to be a dentist anymore.

© 1997 Profiles Corporation. DO NOT DUPLICATE.

6. Who is Zoey?
   A. the dentist's assistant
   B. Willy's mother
   C. Willy's best friend
   D. Willy's sister

7. What does Zoey think has happened to Tyrone's Uncle Mike?
   A. He had a very bad toothache.
   B. He was frightened by Dr. Wolfe.
   C. He has disappeared from River City.
   D. He was eaten by Dr. Wolfe.

8. How was the treatment room different than Willy had expected?
   A. It was much colder.
   B. It was completely empty.
   C. It had blood-red chairs.
   D. It had many dental instruments.

9. What *main* problem is Willy faced with at the end of the passage?
   A. He has to have a cavity filled.
   B. He will soon have his teeth pulled.
   C. He is trapped in a locked room.
   D. He will soon get a shot from Dr. Wolfe.

10. *After* you have read the passage, which of the following is the *best* thing to do to help you understand it better?
    A. Put the main ideas in your own words to make sure you understood the passage.
    B. Reread the passage to make sure you understood each one of the words.
    C. Count the number of paragraphs you can read quickly without stopping.
    D. Have someone else read the passage to you.

© 1997 Profiles Corporation. DO NOT DUPLICATE.